RHS

GARDENER'S
QUIZ & PUZZLE
BOOK

RHS

GARDENER'S
QUIZ &
PUZZLE
BOOK

*100 Brainteasers for Gardeners
Who Know Their Onions*

SIMON AKEROYD &
DR GARETH MOORE

MITCHELL BEAZLEY

RHS Gardener's Quiz and Puzzle Book
Authors: Simon Akeroyd and Gareth Moore
First published in Great Britain in 2019
by Mitchell Beazley, an imprint of
Octopus Publishing Group Ltd,
Carmelite House, 50 Victoria Embankment,
London EC4Y 0DZ

www.octopusbooks.co.uk
An Hachette UK Company
www.hachette.co.uk

Published in association with the
Royal Horticultural Society
© 2019 Quarto Publishing plc

ISBN: 978-1-78472-632-4

A CIP record of this book is available from
the British Library

Printed and bound in China

Mitchell Beazley Publisher: Alison Starling
RHS Head of Editorial: Chris Young
RHS Publisher: Rae Spencer-Jones
RHS Consultant Editor: Simon Maughan

Conceived, designed and produced by
The Bright Press, an imprint of
The Quarto Group
The Old Brewery, 6 Blundell Street
London N7 9BH
United Kingdom
(0)20 7700 6700
www.QuartoKnows.com

Design: Clare Barber and Greg Stalley
Cover: Greg Stalley

The Royal Horticultural Society is the UK's
leading gardening charity dedicated to
advancing horticulture and promoting good
gardening. Its charitable work includes
providing expert advice and information,
training the next generation of gardeners,
creating hands-on opportunities for children
to grow plants and conducting research into
plants, pests and environmental issues
affecting gardeners.

For more information visit www.rhs.org.uk
or call 0845 130 4646.

CONTENTS

How to Use This Book...6

CHAPTER ONE:
Know Your Plants...8

CHAPTER TWO:
Under the Microscope...24

CHAPTER THREE:
Star Gardens...40

CHAPTER FOUR:
Around the World...56

CHAPTER FIVE:
Through the Ages...72

CHAPTER SIX:
Greener Gardening...88

CHAPTER SEVEN:
The Fruit & Veg Patch...102

CHAPTER EIGHT:
Bugs & Beasties...118

CHAPTER NINE:
Branching Out...134

CHAPTER TEN:
The Flowerbed...150

CHAPTER ELEVEN:
Back to Basics...166

Answers...182

Further Resources...206

Picture Credits...207

About the Authors...208

How to Use This Book

This book offers you the chance to pit your horticultural wits against friends and family or just to test your own grey, or should we say green, matter. It is a great way of checking to see if you really do know your onions... or any alliums for that matter.

There are a range of different gardening topics to test your knowledge, with chapters divided up into specialised subjects, including: plant identification; botany and plant science; famous gardens; plants from around the world; garden history; wildlife and green gardening; fruit, vegetables and herbs; shrubs and trees; pests and diseases; herbaceous and annual plants; and gardening basics.

No matter what your level of gardening ability or horticultural knowledge, there are puzzles here to suit both experienced and amateur gardeners. Some are simply multiple-choice or quick-fire rounds on specific subjects, with questions usually becoming more difficult as you work your way through the quiz. Some puzzles ask you to identify plants from their pictures or from other clues. Others are mix-and-match style puzzles, where you have to match up the corresponding pairs. Some ask you to identify who or what is being described by giving you a list of clues, with each one making it easier to work out the subject. How many clues will it take you?

The book is beautifully illustrated throughout, but don't be deceived by all of the images on the pages – some of them are purely decorative. To check if you've successfully solved a puzzle, look at the bottom of the page to be directed to the correct answers, which you'll find at the back of the book.

Chapter One

KNOW YOUR PLANTS

What am I?

How many clues will it take you to work out what I am? Score 10 points if you solve the puzzle with one clue and deduct a point for every additional clue that you need.

1. There over 1,000 types of me growing around the world in 150 countries, although I probably originated as a crop around 7,000 years ago in Papua New Guinea.

2. My leaves and fruit fluoresce in ultraviolet light and I am slightly radioactive.

3. The inside of my skin is supposedly good for polishing shoes and calming the itch of a mosquito bite.

4. My name could be from the West African Wolof language, or possibly derived from the Arabic word for 'finger'.

5. Jules Verne gave a detailed description of me in *Around the World in Eighty Days*.

6. I am the largest herbaceous flowering plant in existence today.

7. I grow from a corm but I am often mistakenly called a tree, although my trunk is actually nothing more than undeveloped leaves.

8. My fruit is produced in tiers called hands.

9. The most popular cultivated variety of me, grown all over the world, is the Cavendish.

10. My crop is mostly eaten as a sweet fruit but another version, called plantain, is usually cooked in savoury dishes.

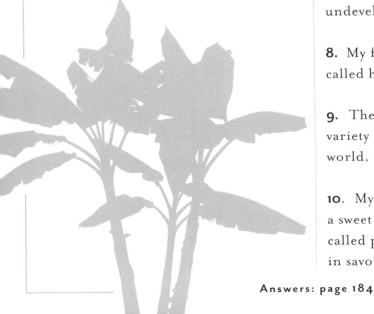

Answers: page 184

Plant portraits

Can you identify the genus of these popular garden plants
from their pictures?

1.

2.

3.

4.

5.

6.

HINT: *The initial letters of the first five plants make up the name of the last one.*

Answers: page 184

The A to Z of plants

Identify these plant genera, listed from A to Z, from the
descriptions that follow. To help you, we have given you the
number of letters in each Latin name.

A _ _ _ _ _ _ _ _ _ – African lily

B _ _ _ _ _ _ _ – evergreen rhizomatous perennial

C _ _ _ _ _ _ _ – cabbage tree from Australia

D _ _ _ _ _ _ _ – poisonous plant

E _ _ _ _ _ _ – plant with milky sap

F _ _ _ _ _ – species called *magellanica*

G _ _ _ _ _ _ _ _ – evergreen hedging plant, New Zealand broadleaf

H _ _ _ _ – evergreen climbers and creepers

I _ _ _ – prickly evergreen, winter berries

J _ _ _ _ _ _ _ – used to flavour gin

K _ _ _ _ _ – yellow-flowering deciduous shrub with lax habit

L _ _ _ _ _ _ _ – scented climber or woody shrub

M _ _ _ _ _ _ – evergreen winter-flowering shrub, blue berries

Answers: page 184

The A to Z of plants (continued)

N _ _ _ _ _ _ — small, dense shrub with autumn foliage, heavenly bamboo

O _ _ _ _ _ _ _ _ — black ornamental grass

P _ _ _ _ _ _ — spring-flowering plant with herbaceous and tree types

Q _ _ _ _ _ _ — mighty trees with huge boughs

R _ _ _ _ _ _ _ — edible, spicy root vegetable, usually red

S _ _ _ _ _ _ _ — ornamental small tree from China and Korea, gives autumn colour

T _ _ _ — evergreen tree with poisonous red berries, source of cancer treatment

U _ _ _ — deciduous tree, many lost to a Dutch disease

V _ _ _ _ _ _ _ — popular shrub: *bodnantense*, *opulus* and *tinus*

W _ _ _ _ _ _ _ _ — genus of about 10 evergreen or deciduous ferns

X _ _ _ _ _ _ _ _ _ — upright rhizomatous perennials from North America

Y _ _ _ _ — spiky evergreen shrub: *elephantipes*, *filamentosa* and *gloriosa*

Z _ _ _ _ _ _ — shrub-like tree from the Mediterranean, autumn foliage

Answers: page 184

Happy families

Match two of the plants below to each of the families listed.

FAMILIES

1. *Rosaceae*
2. *Ericaceae*
3. *Lamiaceae*
4. *Asteraceae*
5. *Iridaceae*
6. *Liliaceae*
7. *Brassicaceae*
8. *Primulaceae*

PLANTS

A. Lettuce
B. Mint
C. *Alyssum*
D. Chives
E. Apple
F. Bilberry
G. Primrose
H. Crocus

I. Oil seed rape
J. Chrysanthemum
K. *Coleus*
L. Aloe
M. Cyclamen
N. Cotoneaster
O. *Gladiolus*
P. Heather

Answers: page 184

Odd one out

Which plant does not belong in the family it is listed beneath?

1. *Apiaceae*
a) Carrot
b) *Eryngium*
c) *Penstemon*
d) *Angelica*

2. *Malvaceae*
a) *Hibiscus*
b) *Edgeworthia*
c) *Abutilon*
d) Hollyhock

3. *Saxifragaceae*
a) *Acer*
b) *Heuchera*
c) *Astilbe*
d) *Bergenia*

4. *Convolvulaceae*
a) *Calystegia sepium*
b) *Convolvulus arvensis*
c) *Ipomoea batatas*
d) *Clematis montana*

5. *Solanaceae*
a) Potato
b) Tomato
c) Tobacco
d) Sweet potato

6. *Apocynaceae*
a) *Dianthus*
b) *Oleander*
c) Frangipani
d) *Mandevilla*

What am I?

How many clues will you need to guess what I am? Score 10 points
if you solve the puzzle with one clue and deduct a point for every
additional clue you need.

1. I'm a genus of flowering plants in the legume family, *Fabaceae*.

2. The botanist Thomas Nuttall named my genus.

3. My leaves are alternate (pinnate) and about 15–35cm (6–14in) long.

4. The world's largest version of me is in California. In 1990 it measured more than 0.4 hectares (1 acre) in size and weighed 250 tons.

5. My two most common forms are Chinese (*sinenis*) and Japanese (*floribunda*).

6. The stems of the Japanese form twine in the opposite direction to those of the Chinese form.

7. I have long, scented, pendulous racemes and mildly toxic pods.

8. I usually have blue-lilac flowers, but I come in pink and white forms as well.

9. I was named after Captain Wistar.

10. All parts of me contain a saponin (a toxic compound) called wisterin.

Answers: page 184

Anagrams: **Cucurbits**

The plants below all belong to the *Cucurbitaceae* family but their letters have been jumbled up. Can you unscramble them to reveal the names of these popular edible food crops?

1. elmno

2. crumbcue

3. ashqus

4. imppunk

5. ecogetrut

6. romraw

7. herking

8. alertwomen

Quick quiz: Green groupings

Green fingers at the ready. Here are some quick-fire quiz
questions to get your horticultural brain cells working.

1. Which family do hawthorn, apple, pear and cherry belong to?

2. Put this popular maple tree in the correct taxonomical sequence — family, genus, species and cultivar: *palmatum*, 'Sango-kaku', *Acer*, *Sapindaceae*.

3. Which genus of plant, with species such as *robusta* and *arabica*, is used to produce a world-famous hot beverage?

4. In the kitchen garden, what types of vegetables would you expect to find in the legumes sections?

5. What are the three largest flowering plant families?

6. Which genus of North American and East Asian tree from swamplands and woods has amazing autumn colour and species including *sylvatica* and *sinensis*?

7. Which genus contains salicin, which is chemically similar to aspirin?

8. *Magnoliaceae* consists of two subfamilies — what are they?

9. What type of plant would you expect to be a member of the *Poaceae* family?

10. What genus of plant from the *Theaceae* family provides growing tips that are used to make the refreshing hot drink known as tea?

11. From the family *Oleaceae* and the genus *Olea*, which European tree produces a flavoursome fruit that is often pressed to produce oil?

12. What material is produced from *Quercus suber* — a member of the oak family — and used around the world?

13. From the asparagus family, *Asparagaceae*, which type of plant are the spirits tequila and mezcal made from?

14. Which family do the fig, banyan, breadfruit and mulberry belong to?

15. Buttercups, anemones, delphiniums and aquilegias all belong to which family?

Answers: page 185

QUESTION 14

What am I?

How many clues will you require before you can guess what plant
I am? Score 10 points if you solve the puzzle with one clue and
deduct a point for each additional clue that you need.

1. I belong to the *Polygonaceae* family.

2. I am native to East Asian
countries including Japan, China
and Korea.

3. I am a clump-forming perennial.

4. I spread underground
via rhizomes.

5. My leaves can be described as
heart- or shovel-shaped and are
up to 14cm (5½in) in length.

6. I produce creamy-white
flower tassels in late summer
and early autumn.

7. I have bamboo-like stems that
are flecked with purple and grow
to 2.1m (7ft) tall.

8. I am an invasive weed and can
grow through patios and roads.

9. In some countries it is illegal to
cause this plant to grow in the wild.

10. In some countries if I'm present
in the garden of a property being
sold, it must be declared – and I can
render the property unmortgageable.

Plant IDs

Can you identify these members of the *Asteraceae* family
from their pictures?

1.

2.

3.

4.

5.

6.

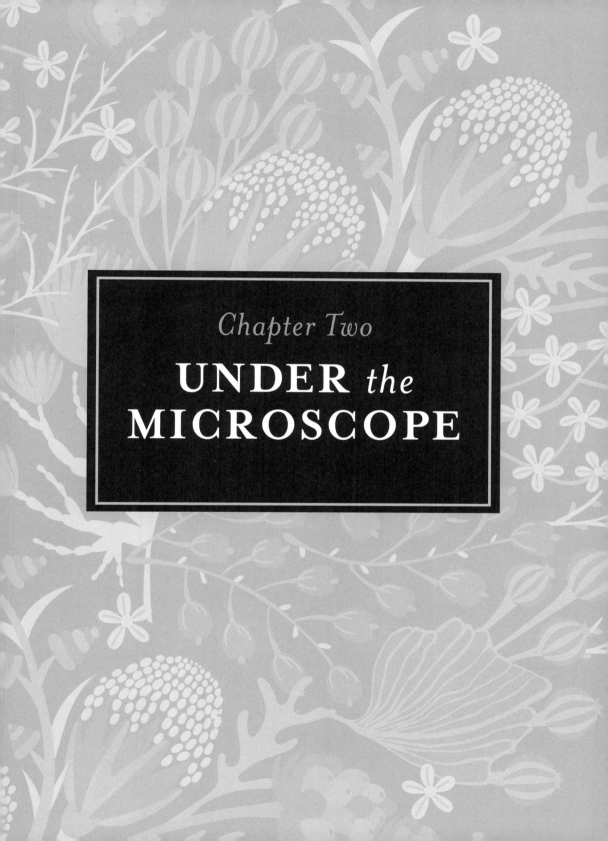

Chapter Two

UNDER *the* MICROSCOPE

Colour clues

Gardeners often use plants to create a splash of colour in the
garden. They can be used in design schemes ranging from bright,
vibrant colours to calm, subdued pastel tones. But can you tell
what colour a plant is purely from its botanical name? Match
these Latin botanical descriptions to their equivalent colours.

BOTANICAL DESCRIPTIONS

1. *Lutea*
2. *Carneus*
3. *Caerulae*
4. *Sanguinea*

5. *Argenteus*
6. *Viridis*
7. *Alba*
8. *Coccineus*

A. Pale pink

B. White

C. Yellow

D. Scarlet

E. Blood red

F. Blue

G. Silver

H. Green

The language of leaves

Plants aren't all about flowers. Many gardeners select plants for the architectural and textural qualities of their leaves, which can range enormously in size, shape and colour. Can you match the images of the leaves below to their botanical foliage descriptions?

1.

2.

3.

4.

5.

6.

7.

8.

BOTANICAL FOLIAGE DESCRIPTORS

A. *Aquifolius* **B.** *Palmate* **C.** *Rotundifolia* **D.** *Pinnata* **E.** *Microphylla*
F. *Cordate* **G.** *Quercifolia* **H.** *Longifolia*

Mix and match: **Location, location, location**

A plant's species name can reveal its natural habitat.
Can you work out the location where you would expect to find
each of these plants according to their species names?

BOTANICAL DESCRIPTIONS

1. *Palustris*
2. *Maritime*
3. *Hortensis*
4. *Insularis*
5. *Riparius*

6. *Saxatilis*
7. *Campestris*
8. *Montana*
9. *Muralis*
10. *Sylvestris*

LOCATIONS

A. Mountains
B. Islands
C. Marshes or wetlands
D. Walls
E. Forests
F. Rocks
G. Gardens
H. Fields
I. Riverbanks
J. Coasts

Anagrams: **Subterranean structures**

Unravel the anagrams below to reveal different types of roots
or underground stems and storage systems for plants.

1. **ifrobus**

2. **apt**

3. **zerohim**

4. **brute**

5. **lubb**

6. **noslot**

7. **crom**

8. **auditionsvet**

Answers: page 186

Mix and match: The global garden

Our gardens are home to plants originating from many corners
of the world. Can you match each botanical name below to
the plant's country of origin?

Botanical names

1. *Sinensis*
2. *Aethiopium*
3. *Helveticus*
4. *Hispanicus*
5. *Gallicus*
6. *Cambrica*
7. *Lusitanica*
8. *Himalaica*
9. *Graeca*
10. *Japonica*

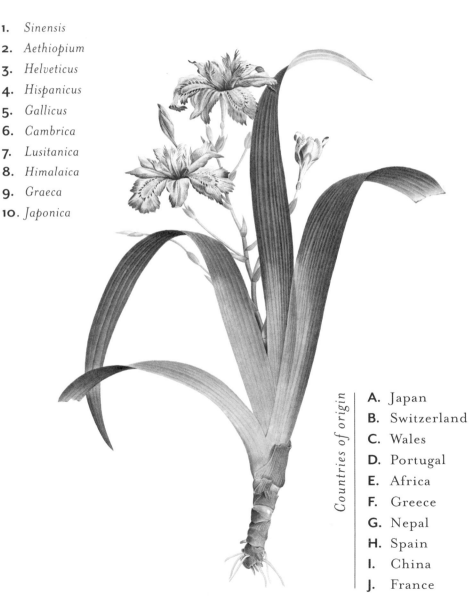

Countries of origin

A. Japan
B. Switzerland
C. Wales
D. Portugal
E. Africa
F. Greece
G. Nepal
H. Spain
I. China
J. France

Multiple-choice: What's in a name?

The botanical name given to a plant can help a gardener to
understand its key attributes. Can you work out what the
following Latin words mean when they appear in a plant name?

1. If a plant has the descriptive word
somnifera in its name, what effect would
you expect it to have if eaten or smelled?

a) *Excitement*

b) *Hallucinations*

c) *Sleep*

d) *Vomiting*

2. What would you anticipate feeling if
you handled a plant with the word *viscosa*
in its botanical name?

a) *Spikes*

b) *Stickiness*

c) *Stings*

d) *Velvety leaves*

3. Why was *Daphne odorata* given
the species name *odorata*?

a) *It has an upright habit*

b) *It flowers in winter*

c) *It has evergreen foliage*

d) *It is scented*

4. Lots of plants have *borealis* as their
botanical species name to denote their
geographical location. Where would
you expect a plant with this name to
come from?

a) *North*

b) *East*

c) *South*

d) *West*

5. What does it mean if a plant has the
word *edulis* in its name?

a) *It grows on the edge of woodlands*

b) *Part of the plant is edible*

c) *It was discovered during the reign of
Edward the Confessor*

d) *It grows near water eddies by riverbanks*

6. If a plant is described as having
a *scandens* habit, what sort of growth
would you expect?

a) *Creeping*

b) *Prostrate*

c) *Climbing*

d) *Pendulous*

The answer lies in the soil

The success of a garden is very often dependent on placing the right plant in the correct soil. Can you match up these common types of garden soil with their descriptions?

SOIL TYPES

A. Chalky soil   **C.** Silt soil   **E.** Sandy soil
B. Peat soil   **D.** Loam soil   **F.** Clay soil

1. Light and warm with large particles, gritty to the touch, often acidic and easy to dig. This type of soil is quick to warm up in spring but can dry out quickly in summer and suffer from low nutrients. Often referred to as 'hungry' soil.

2. Dark in colour, very high in organic matter, with superb moisture-retaining qualities. It is unusual in the garden but often brought in as a soil improver, used in hanging baskets or to grow annual bedding plants. Its overuse has become a contentious issue, with many gardeners looking for alternatives.

3. Sticky to the touch and rolls into a ball easily without crumbling when moulded in your hand. Known by gardeners as a heavy soil, it is often dreaded if digging is required. It tends to stay wet and cold in winter, but in summer dries out quickly, often baking as hard as a brick. It is, however, usually high in nutrients and retains organic matter well.

4. Very pale in colour, sometimes completely white, often stony. This type of soil can be light or heavy but is always high in alkalinity and is unsuitable for ericaceous plants. It is usually quite porous, with an ideal combination of good drainage, moisture and nutrient-retaining qualities.

5. A mix of sand, silt and clay make this the dream soil type for most garden plants. It has many of the benefits of the other soils, but without the negatives. It is usually fertile and easy to cultivate and has good drainage. This type of soil warms up quickly in spring and yet won't dry out in summer.

6. A light and moisture-retentive soil that has good levels of fertility. The texture when touched is often said to be smooth and 'soapy'. It is easy to cultivate but has poor soil structure and is easily compacted if walked over.

Answers: page 186

Multiple-choice: Down and dirty

Successful gardening very much depends on an understanding of the soil conditions. Test your knowledge of soil with these multiple-choice questions.

1. Complete the name of this soil measurement: Cation ..... capacity

a) *Matrix*

b) *Exchange*

c) *Crumbly*

d) *Subsoil*

2. What does double digging involve?

a) *Planting two plants to increase survival chances*

b) *Digging down to two spade depths and adding organic matter*

c) *Cultivating two allotments to double your yield*

d) *Employing two gardeners to dig a planting hole*

3. Plants that prefer acidic soil are known as what?

a) *Burnicaceous*

b) *Sulphurcaceous*

c) *Acidificaceous*

d) *Ericaceous*

4. What type of soil do most rhododendrons, camellias and magnolias generally require?

a) *Chalky*

b) *Limestone*

c) *Acidic*

d) *Water-logged*

5. What soil pH is neutral?

a) *2.2*

b) *3.1*

c) *4.5*

d) *7.0*

6. What are gardeners referring to when they mention NPK?

a) *Nitrogen, phosphorus and potassium*

b) *Never Pick Kale*

c) *Nitrogen, potassium and iron*

d) *Nicotine, potassium and krypton*

Answers: page 186

Plant parts

Identify the different parts of the plant indicated by the labels
in the diagram below.

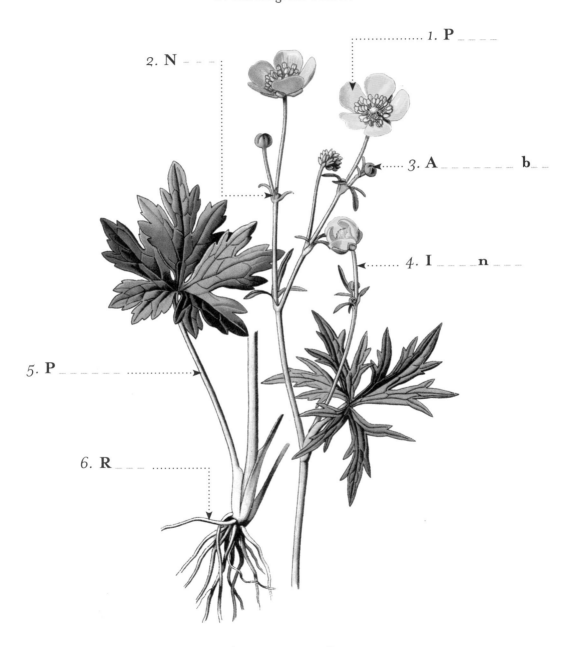

1. **P** _ _ _ _

2. **N** _ _ _

3. **A** _ _ _ _ _ _ _ _ _ _ _ **b** _ _

4. **I** _ _ _ _ **n** _ _ _

5. **P** _ _ _ _ _ _ _ _

6. **R** _ _ _ _

Answers: page 187

Multiple-choice: Biological brainteasers

Test your knowledge of plant processes and physiology
with these multiple-choice questions.

1. What is auxin?

a) The cell wall

b) The growing tip

c) A growth hormone

d) Bacteria in the stem

2. What is abscission?

a) Leaf fall

b) Division of cell

c) A split stem

d) A double flower

3. What type of dominance in a plant does 'apical dominance' refer to?

a) Water over solids

b) Lead bud over laterals

c) Sand moving through clay

d) Warm water being displaced with cold

4. What is osmosis?

a) The process of stem decay

b) The movement of moisture from high concentration to low

c) Reactive growth from a wound

d) Root elongation

5. What function does the xylem have?

a) Carrying water and minerals from the roots to the stems and leaves

b) Disposing of waste liquids through stomata

c) Carrying sugar and other organic nutrients from the leaves to rest of the plant

d) Disposing of excess carbohydrates through leaf axils

6. What is plant morphology the study of?

a) The physical form and external structure of plants

b) The artistic recreation of plants using modelling clay

c) Habitats of alpine plants outside of the Alps

d) The ability of plants to blend into the landscape

7. What is the process of water moving through the plant and out through the stomata in the leaves called?

a) Aqualation

b) Mortification

c) Tricklefication

d) Transpiration

Answers: page 187

Mix and match: **Taxing taxonomy**

The words on the right are all botanical descriptors for the humble apple. Can you match them with the taxonomic ranks on the left?

Taxonomic rank

1. Domain
2. Kingdom
3. Division
4. Class
5. Order
6. Family
7. Genus
8. Species
9. Cultivar

Apple descriptors

A. *domestica*
B. 'Worcester Pearmain'
C. *Rosales*
D. Eukarya
E. *Rosaceae*
F. Magnoliopsida
G. Magnoliophyta
H. Plantae
I. *Malus*

Anatomy of a flower

Test your knowledge of botanical terminology by naming the flower parts shown in the diagram below.

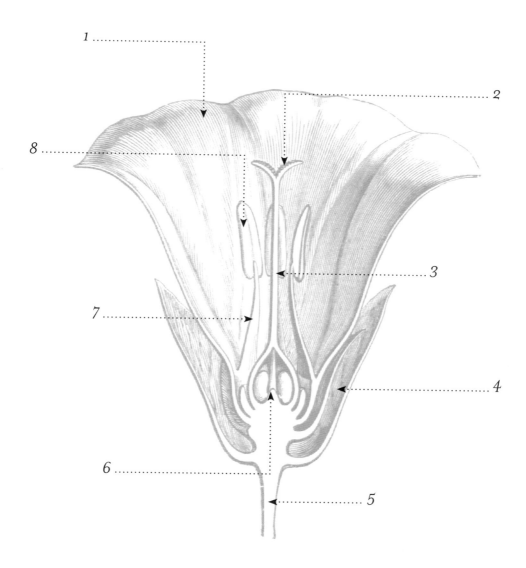

Mix and match: Botanical breakthroughs

Can you match up the person who made a major contribution to plant science with the clue and their country of origin?

BOTANIST OR PERSON

1. Charles Darwin
2. Matthias Jakob Schleiden
3. Joseph Dalton Hooker
4. William Bartram
5. Antoine Augustin Parmentier

6. Janaki Ammal
7. Carl Linnaeus
8. Hugo von Mohl
9. Nikolai Vavilov
10. Jan Ingenhousz

BREAKTHROUGHS

A. Best known for being the discoverer of photosynthesis (Dutch)

B. Scientist famous for identifying, naming and classifying organisms (Swedish)

C. Director of Kew Gardens for over 20 years (British)

D. Wrote *On the Origin of Species* (British)

E. Credited with recognising and naming protoplasm and proposing that cells divide to form new cells (German)

F. Travelled across South America and discovered several plant species, including the Franklin tree (*Franklinia alatamaha*) (USA)

G. A geneticist who worked for RHS Garden Wisley in the early 1950s, and investigated the effects of colchicine on a number of woody plants, including magnolia (Indian)

H. Attempted to resolve the problem of starvation in Russia, but was imprisoned under Stalin for 20 years and tragically died of starvation in a prison camp (Russian)

I. Promoter of the potato as a food source (French)

J. Concluded that all plant tissues are composed of cells (German)

Anagrams: Scrambled science

Unravel these anagrams to reveal words often
used in plant biology.

1. cyandorm

2. ickytnsion

3. naystanchion

4. optsrainier

5. aminitrogen

6. englibrelibs

7. hollylochpr

8. alloinpoint

9. heatpong

10. lavascur suites

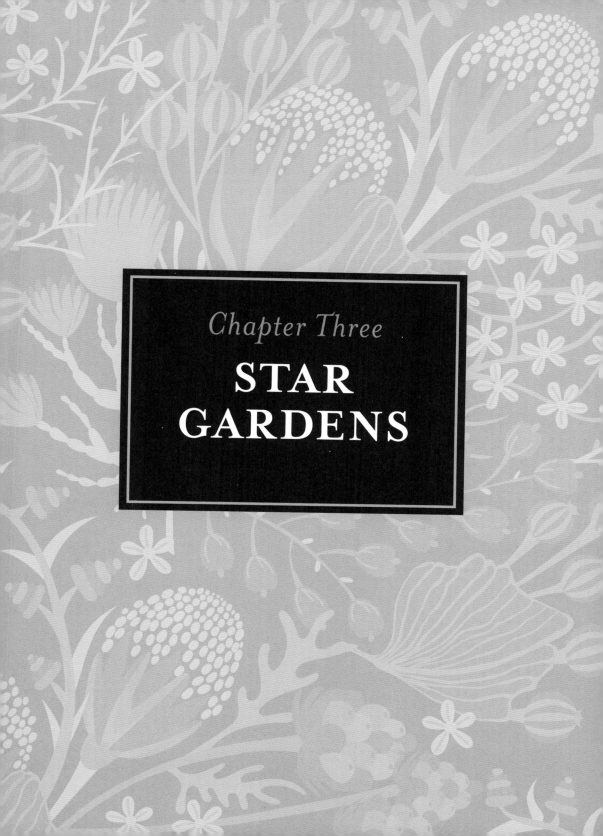

Chapter Three

STAR GARDENS

Around the world in 10 gardens

On the left are some of the most exciting and fascinating gardens in the world. Can you match the names of the gardens to the cities and countries they can be found in? Once you've paired up the gardens with their respective cities, see if you can match them with their locations on the map.

GARDENS

1. Jardim Botânico
2. Shalimar Gardens
3. Kirstenbosch National Botanic Garden
4. Akatsuka Botanical Garden
5. Fairchild Tropical Botanic Garden
6. Jardin des Plantes
7. Nong Nooch Tropical Botanical Garden
8. Jardin d'Essais
9. Patscherkofel Alpine Garden
10. Jardin de Cactus

CITIES

A. Cape Town, South Africa

B. Rio de Janeiro, Brazil

C. Guatiza, Lanzarote, Canary Islands

D. Pattaya, Thailand

E. Tokyo, Japan

F. Lahore, Pakistan

G. Innsbruck, Austria

H. Paris, France

I. Rabat, Morocco

J. Miami, USA

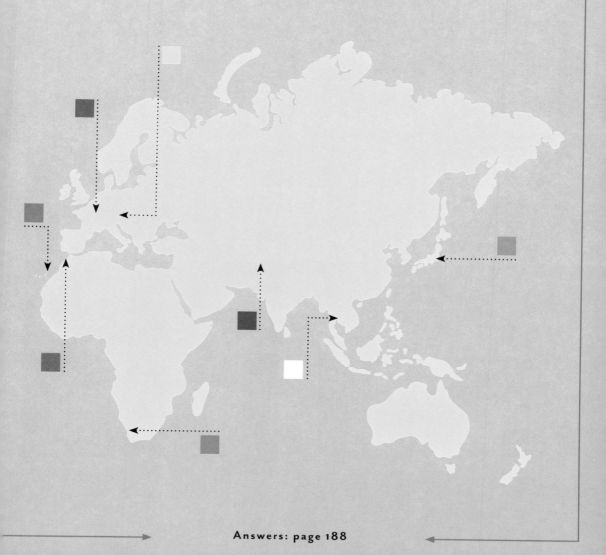

Answers: page 188

Who am I?

Which famous British horticulturist and writer do these clues
describe? Score 10 points if you can solve the puzzle with one
clue and deduct a point for each additional clue that you need.

1. I lived between 9 March 1892 and
2 June 1962.

2. As well as being a celebrated
gardener, I also won awards for
writing and poetry.

3. In the Southeast of England I
created one of the most visited gardens
in the country.

4. This world-renowned garden was
donated to the National Trust in 1967.

5. My style of garden design was
influenced by Hidcote Manor and
the Arts and Crafts movement, and
typically involved creating a series
of 'rooms'.

6. The garden features a Tudor tower,
with views over the Wealden valley,
which I used to write in.

7. The White Garden is one of the
most celebrated features of the garden.

8. I was married to diplomat and
writer Harold Nicholson, but had an
open marriage and famously had an
affair with Virginia Woolf.

9. The garden sits on what was once
a Saxon pig farm, originally called
Saxenhurst.

10. My garden was called Sissinghurst.

I HAD A PASSIONATE AFFAIR
WITH VIRGINIA WOOLF

Answer: page 188

Anagrams: Mixed-up gardens

Can you unscramble the following anagrams? They are all gardens
famed for their plant collections or exceptional design.

1. raylo cabinto dragens ewk

2. waterfallgin

3. itiso borerot bluer axmr

4. acuteha ed navydrill

5. el ranjid reamjello

6. eekfunkoh danger

7. damenuts dowo

8. het musemr ranged

Answers: page 188

Multiple-choice: **Gardens of the world**

Answer these multiple-choice questions to test
your knowledge of global gardens.

1. This garden benefits from the warming currents of the Gulf Stream despite its northerly location. It hosts a wealth of lush subtropical planting, including the Wollemi pine, the blue Himalayan poppy and Chinese rhododendrons. What is it called?

a) *Mount Stewart*

b) *Inverewe Garden*

c) *Dawyck Botanic Garden*

d) *Royal Botanical Gardens, Edinburgh*

2. One of the most influential designers of the 21st century, this Dutch landscaper has grown a reputation for massed perennial planting in a naturalistic style. His work includes some famous public projects in New York City, including Battery Park and the High Line, a disused section of elevated train track repurposed as a green space. What is his name?

a) *Piet Oudolf*

b) *Mien Ruys*

c) *Famke Janssen*

d) *Jacque Dunker*

3. Which of the following gardens is not owned by the Royal Horticultural Society?

a) *Rosemoor*

b) *Tatton Park*

c) *Harlow Carr*

d) *Hyde Hall*

4. Ryōan-ji in Kyoto, Japan is a famous example of a Zen garden. It contains only three symbolic elements and is considered to be the most abstract of all the Zen gardens of Japan. What are the three elements?

a) *Black pines, gravel, moss*

b) *Grass, water, air*

c) *Topiary shapes, gravel, stones*

d) *Gravel, stones, moss*

5. Designated a National Historic Site of Canada, these gardens are situated on Vancouver Island and welcome over a million visitors a year. They are named for the wealthy couple who first began developing the estate. What are the gardens called?

a) *The Butchart Gardens*

b) *Annapolis Royal Historic Garden*

c) *Jardin de Metis*

d) *Kingsbrae Garden*

Answers: page 188

Name the garden

Can you identify the garden that is shown in the four pictures below?

Answer: page 188

Quick quiz: **Know your gardens**

Answer these quick-fire questions to test your
knowledge of famous gardens.

1. Australia's National Botanic Garden
is located in which city?

2. Who is primarily responsible for
creating the Eden Project?

3. Hall's Croft in Stratford-upon-Avon
is located opposite the church where a
famous English playwright was laid to
rest. Who was the playwright?

4. The world's largest flower
garden, containing around
60 million flowering plants,
was built over desert sand in
which city in the United Arab
Emirates? What is it called?

5. Where is the Karoo Desert
National Botanical Garden?

6. Waterperry Gardens opened
as a horticultural college in
1932. What was special about
its students?

7. The fantasy Italianate Gardens
of Portmeirion in Wales are famous
as the backdrop to which cult 1960s'
television series?

8. The Gartenanlage-Gedenkstätte in
Brandenberg, Germany, was designed by
Karl Foerster. With which group of plants
is he mostly commonly associated?

STUDENTS AT WATERPERRY HORTICULTURAL COLLEGE IN 1943

Answers: page 188

What kind of garden am I?

Select the word or phrase that correctly describes each garden below.

1. Westonbirt, England
Arboretum • Contemporary • Botanic Garden

2. Mount Vernon, USA
Park • 18th-century landscape • Naturalistic

3. Castle of Mey, Scotland
Formal • Cottage garden • Pinetum

4. Bay Gardens, Grenada
Tropical jungle • Caribbean colonial • Naturalistic

5. Villa Medici, Italy
15th-century Renaissance • Italianate • Topiary

6. Parc de Bagatelle, France
Modern park • Rose garden • Pleasure park

7. Kenrokuen, Japan
Stroll garden • Temple garden • Scholar's garden

8. Bagh-e Fin, Iran
Persian chahar bagh • Water garden • Palmery

Answers: page 188

Which century?

These famous gardens and parks are all excellent representatives
of particular historical garden styles – and very much of their time.
Can you match them to the right century?

CENTURIES

17th and 18th century • 19th century • 20th century

GARDENS

A. Mount Stewart,
County Down, Ireland

B. Central Park, *New York, USA*

C. Felbrigg Hall, *Norfolk, England*

D. Taliesin, *Wisconsin, USA*

E. The Garden of Cosmic
Speculation, *Dumfries, Scotland*

F. Rowallane Garden,
County Down, Ireland

G. Oxford Botanic Garden,
Oxford, England

H. Chateau de Fontainebleau,
Fontainebleau, France

I. Biddulph Grange,
Stoke-on-Trent, England

J. Levens Hall, *Cumbria, England*

K. The Lost Gardens of Heligan,
Cornwall, England

L. Park Güell, *Barcelona, Spain*

M. Waddesdon Manor,
Buckinghamshire, England

N. Paleis Het Loo,
Amsterdam, Netherlands

O. La Pozas, *Xilitla, Mexico*

P. Gravetye Manor, *Sussex, England*

Q. Beth Chatto Gardens,
Essex, England

R. Tivoli, *Copenhagen, Denmark*

S. Stourhead, *Wiltshire, England*

T. Taj Mahal, *Agra, India*

U. Coleton Fishacre, *Devon, England*

Answers: page 189

THE TAJ MAHAL GARDENS, PAINTED BY ERASTUS SALISBURY FIELD

Mix and match: Famous for being famous

It's not just design professionals who can make a garden famous. Many notable people have made their mark in the garden world. Can you match the famous faces to the correct gardens? If you're struggling to work out who's who, we've given you their names below.

FAMOUS FACES

1.

2.

3.

4.

5.

6.

7.

8.

9.

HINT: 1. *Prince Charles,* 2. *Anne Boleyn,* 3. *Beatrix Potter,* 4. *Thomas Jefferson,* 5. *Frida Kahlo,* 6. *Yves Saint Laurent,* 7. *Empress Josephine,* 8. *Winston Churchill,* 9. *Agatha Christie*

MONTICELLO GARDENS, PAINTED BY JANE BRADDICK

GARDENS

A. Hill Top

B. Casa Azul

C. Hever Castle

D. Greenway

E. Chateau de Malmaison

F. Highgrove House

G. Monticello

H. Jardin Majorelle

I. Chartwell

Answers: page 189

Famous garden facts

Identify the missing words to complete the sentences below.

1. Possibly the most beautiful of the M _ _ g Dynasty Gardens in China, Liu Yuan in Suzhou is renowned for its rock and stone formations.

2. Lanzarote's arid landscape is home to the Jardin del C _ _ _ _ s, created by César Manrique as a living artwork combining succulents and contemporary sculpture.

3. The Museum of Garden History, site of the Tradescant family tomb, can be found adjacent to L _ _ _ _ _ h Palace, the official London residence of the Archbishop of Canterbury.

4. The oldest arboretum in the USA, bequeathed by a whaling merchant to the University of H _ _ _ _ _ d, is around 107 hectares (265 acres) in size and contains more than 14,000 plants.

5. The 16th-century Italian Sacro Bosco, (meaning sacred wood), contains macabre sculptures of giants, dragons and demons. It's known locally as the 'Park of M _ _ _ _ _ _ s'.

What am I?

I am one of the most impressive gardens in the world with over half a million visitors a year – but what is my name? Can you work it out from the clues below? Score 10 points if you solve the puzzle with one clue and deduct a point for each extra clue that you need.

1. I stretch over 19 hectares (47 acres) and look towards a Sugar Loaf Mountain.

2. Created in the 19th century by Mervyn Wingfield, the 7th Viscount of the estate, I took around 20 years to complete.

3. My design was inspired by visits to the Palace of Versailles, Schönbrunn Palace near Vienna and the Schwetzingen Castle near Heidelberg.

4. I am currently owned by the Slazenger family, but I am open to the public all year round.

5. My Palladian house burned down almost completely in the 1970s, but has since been rebuilt.

6. One of my features, Pepperpot Tower, is supposedly designed after the favourite pepper pot of Lady Wingfield, Anne Boleyn's lady-in-waiting.

7. Within my grounds you can find both Japanese and Italian features, walled gardens and a pet cemetery.

8. My water features include the Dolphin Pond, Triton Lake and a nearby 121m (397ft) waterfall.

9. National Geographic recently voted me the third best garden in the world.

10. I can be found in County Wicklow, in Ireland.

Answer: page 189

Chapter Four

AROUND the WORLD

Mix and match: Global roots

Scientists estimate that there are nearly 400,000 plant species on our planet. They have colonised almost every available corner and adapted to an enormous variety of climates and situations. Today's gardeners have access to a plethora of wonderful species and we can easily take all this choice for granted. This chapter will test your knowledge about the origins of the plants you grow. You might be surprised to learn where they originally come from!

The plants on the left are all commonly grown the world over, but can you match them to their original country or region of origin?

Plants

1. Petunia
2. Pelargonium Geranium
3. Garden sage
4. Zinnia
5. Bougainvillea
6. Phormium
7. Rhubarb
8. Apple
9. Houseleek
10. Aspidistra

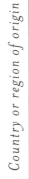

Country or region of origin

A. South East Asia
B. The Americas, particularly Mexico
C. Central Asia
D. Middle East
E. South America
F. Mediterranean
G. Brazil/Argentina
H. Southern Africa and Australia
I. New Zealand
J. China

Answers: page 190

Beyond borders

Plants have adapted to thrive in many different environments, known as
biomes. A biome is a community of plants and animals that share adapted
characteristics designed to ensure survival within their environment.
They can be found over a range of continents and are not country-specific.
Can you group the following plant species into the correct biomes?

BIOMES

1. Tundra
2. Taiga (also called boreal forest)
3. Temperate deciduous forest
4. Scrubland (called chaparral in
   California)

5. Grassland (savannah or prairie)
6. Desert
7. Tropical rainforest
8. Temperate rainforest

PLANTS

A. *Agave americana*
B. *Echinocactus grusonii*
C. *Salix arctica*
D. *Abies balsamea*
E. *Pseudotsuga menziesii*
F. *Victoria amazonica*
G. *Rafflesia arnoldii*
H. *Beaucarnea recurvata*

I. *Nothofagus dombeyi*
J. *Quercus robur*
K. *Silene acaulis*
L. *Eucalyptus gregsoniana*
M. *Picea obovata*
N. *Monstera deliciosa*
O. *Pennisetum purpureum*
P. *Cynodon dactylon*

Q. *Ledum groenlandium*
R. *Panicum virgatum*
S. *Athyrium filix-femina*
T. *Polypodium glycyrrhiza*
U. *Acer pseudoplatanus*
V. *Larix sibirica*
W. *Myrtus communis*
X. *Artemisia abrotanum*

HINT: *There are three plants in each group.*

What am I?

Can you work out the Latin name of each of the following plants based on their descriptions?

1. Grown and eaten by the Aztecs, who called me cocoxochitl, I am a tuberous native of Mexico. Today I am grown for my showy flowers, which, due to my complex chromosome make-up, come in a wide range of colours and types, including 'cactus', 'waterlily' and 'pom-pom'.

2. One of the oldest fruit trees in cultivation, I have been a favourite in Chinese culture for over 2,000 years. I am deciduous and usually either male or female, although I sometimes vary my sexuality from year to year, and can even be both at the same time. My fruit is orange and slightly astringent, and when ripe my pulp has a jelly-like consistency. I am sold as persimmon or Sharon fruit.

3. I am a plant loved by children for my extraordinary abilities. Native to wetlands on the east coast of the USA I cannot absorb nutrients from the brackish water so instead I have become carnivorous, trapping unwary insects between my sensitive, trigger-happy leaves. If the tiny hairs on my open leaves are stimulated in succession I can snap them together in around a tenth of a second, locking in my prey.

4. I am a popular houseplant and tolerant of shade but I also have a dark reputation; my cells contain needle-shaped calcium oxalate crystals called raphides, which cause the throat of anyone or anything that tries to eat me to swell up. Numbness, pain and drooling are also a possibility, although rumours that I am deadly are exaggerated. I am a native of the American tropics, with glossy leaves, which are often spotted or marked.

HINT: *All of the answers begin with the letter D.*

National flowers

Can you identify the country that is associated with each
of these national flowers?

1. *Erythrina crista-galli*
**Argentina • France
Costa Rica**

2. *Leontopodium alpinum*
Poland • Switzerland • Germany

3. *Acer saccharum*
Canada • Jamaica • Japan

4. *Nelumbo nucifera*
Thailand • Vietnam • India

5. *Cirsium altissimum*
Norway • Scotland • Ireland

6. *Gloriosa superba* 'Rothschildiana'
USA • Zimbabwe • South Africa

7. *Bauhinia blakeana*
**Thailand • Philippines
Hong Kong**

8. *Acanthus mollis*
**Greece • Italy
Turkey**

Answers: page 190

Anagrams: **The mother of all gardens**

A famous plant collector once referred to China as 'the mother of all gardens', which is unsurprising when you realise that the country is home to one-eighth of the world's plant species. Unscramble the following Latin names to identify garden plants, shrubs and trees, all of which originally come from this extraordinary country.

1. *aidavid lucrativano*
Deciduous tree with distinctive white bracts and hard nuts

2. *jabdudel viadidi*
Butterfly-attracting shrub that flowers on new wood each year

3. *animalgo dialviaye*
Large evergreen tree with big, glossy leaves and magnificent cream flowers

4. *soar nichesins*
Thorny, repeat-flowering shrub cultivated since ancient times

5. *meanone sheepishnu*
Clump-forming perennial with striking flowers on long, wiry stems that blossom in late summer or autumn

6. *odddronehorn reintofu*
Fragrant evergreen shrub from high altitude, which flowers late for the species

7. *asplotchshyly idleus*
Fast-growing, hardy plant that is often used as timber or for tool-making; covered in fine hairs and can grow to 8m (26ft) tall

What am I?

How many clues will it take for you to guess what I am? Score
10 points if you solve the puzzle with one clue and deduct
a point for each additional clue that you need.

1. Thomas Edison used me to develop
his first mass-produced electric bulbs.

2. I am a member of the *Poaceae* family
and therefore a monocot.

3. If eaten raw my young shoots contain
a toxin called taxiphyllin.

4. I rarely flower, but when I do, all
plants derived from the same clonal
stock, no matter where in the world,
will flower at the same time.

5. I grow from an underground tuber,
as a fully formed culm.

6. I am the fastest-growing plant on
earth, able to grow up to 1m (3ft) in
24 hours if conditions are suitable.

7. I am the inspiration for fireworks
and guns, as my hollow stems
are compartmentalised and pop
loudly when burnt.

8. I release more oxygen into the
atmosphere and absorb more carbon
dioxide than any other group of plants.

9. There are over 1,000 species of me,
including garden favourites such as
Phyllostachys nigra and *Fargesia nitida*.

10. I am a panda's favourite food.

What am I?

As beautiful as flowers are, one of the main reasons people garden around the world is to feed themselves and their families. Throughout history people have cultivated plants for survival as much as for pleasure and, today, many plants are staple domesticated crops that keep whole nations economically viable and millions of people in work. Can you identify some of the most interesting crops from the descriptions below?

1. Native to the Amazon basin, I can trace my history back to the Olmec civilisation over 4,000 years ago. As I will grow within 20 degrees of latitude of the equator, about 70 per cent of my total volume now comes from West Africa. Linnaeus named me the 'food of the Gods' when classifying me, and I have a reputation as being a luxury beverage or snack.

2. I provide more than one-fifth of the total calories consumed by Earth's human population, yet my individual leaves are less than 3cm (1.2in) wide. My parent species are native to Asia and Africa. I am usually grown in flooded fields, which helps prevent pest and weed infestations, but it is not strictly necessary. My edible seeds are the staple food of half the world's human population.

3. A large climber, I produce fuzzy fruit that gained in worldwide popularity in the last century. I am often associated with one antipodean country, due to my apparent resemblance to a flightless bird, although I am actually Chinese in origin. Modern varieties of me are self-fertile but traditionally gardeners would have to plant both a male and female plant to ensure a good crop.

4. I am one of the first cultivated grains, and my wild ancestor is still abundant in the Fertile Crescent where human civilisation really took off. I grow well in temperate climates, and Russia, France and Germany are all big producers of me today. In Europe, I am primarily an ingredient in beer, bread and whisky, but am also used as a staple food in other countries.

Answers: page 191

Which continent?

Can you identify which continents the following plants originate from?

1.

2.

3.

4.

5.

Which country are we from?

The following plants all originate from the same country – but can
you work out which country?

1. *Justicia spicigera*
A honeysuckle-type plant

2. *Graptopetalum amethystinum*
An altitude-loving succulent

3. *Ipomoea purpurea*
A climbing morning glory

4. *Mexipedium xerophyticum*
A rare orchid

5. *Agave sisalana*
The source of sisal, a stiff fibre used
to make ropes and matting

6. *Polianthes tuberosa*
A fragrant lily bulb

7. *Cephalocereus senilis*
The old man cactus

8. *Euphorbia pulcherrima*
A Christmas speciality

9. *Picea chihuahuana*
A small pine

Answer: page 191

Multiple-choice: Wicked world

The world is full of plants that seem programmed to cause death and injury to humans. How well do you know your horticultural horrors?

1. This tree from India is the source of one of the world's nastiest and most painful poisons, traditionally used to kill rats, which causes severe muscle spasms and usually death.

a) *Ficus lyrata*

b) *Strychnos nux–vomica*

c) *Atropa belladonna*

d) *Azadirachta indica*

2. This European plant, found in wet areas throughout the Northern Hemisphere, can be easily confused with other more benign umbellifers. A poisonous drink made from this plant was reportedly responsible for the death of the Greek philosopher Socrates.

a) *Daucus carota*

b) *Heracleum mantegazzianum*

c) *Conium maculatum*

d) *Apium graveolens*

3. Toxic enough that over 90 million people worldwide have died because of it, this plant has a lot to answer for but growing it remains a lucrative business. Containing a highly addictive substance, it has been cultivated for nearly 7,000 years.

a) *Papaver somniferum*

b) *Elaeis guineensis*

c) *Nicotiana langsdorffii*

d) *Nicotiana tabacum*

4. This dramatic-looking annual/tender perennial, with huge palmate leaves and prickly seed pods, makes a wonderful addition to a hot tropical-style border – but the seeds will do more than just heat you up. They are the source of a slow-acting but deadly poison that is a stalwart in the world of spies.

a) *Fatsia japonica*

b) *Ricinus communis*

c) *Cynara cardunculus*

d) *Tetrapanax papyrifer*

Answers: page 191

Mediterranean marvels

The Mediterranean Basin plays host to a fantastic variety of plants that, thanks to human intervention, have spread widely throughout the region itself and even across the entire world. Can you identify these classic Mediterranean plants from their pictures? We've provided the first letter of each name to get you started.

1. **P**

2. **O**

3. **L**

4. **P**

5. **T**

6. **R**

Answers: page 191

America versus Asia

Can you identify which of these plants originate
from the Americas and which from Asia?

PLANTS

A. *Paeonia delavayi*
B. *Chaenomeles speciosa*
C. *Pseudotsuga menziesii*
D. *Wisteria sinensis*
E. *Helianthus annuus*
F. *Meconopsis betonicifolia*
G. *Fuchsia magellanica*
H. *Viburnum farreri*
I. *Camellia saluenensis*
J. *Victoria amazonica*
K. *Sequoiadendron giganteum*
L. *Fatsia Japonica*
M. *Passiflora caerulea*
N. *Amelanchier canadensis*
O. *Pinus radiata*
P. *Aucuba japonica*
Q. *Acer palmatum*
R. *Agave americana*
S. *Rhododendron sinogrande*
T. *Canna indica*

MECONOPSIS BETONICIFOLIA

Answers: page 191

Island natives

The following plants are native to one or more islands of the
world. In many cases their island isolation means they are
endemic to that one place. Can you match each plant to the
island or group of islands from which it originates?

Plants

1. *Catharanthus roseus*
2. *Myosotidium hortensia*
3. *Sorbus groenlandica*
4. *Amorphophallus titanum*
5. *Gossypium darwinii*
6. *Hedera azorica*
7. *Sasa nipponica*
8. *Acacia koa*
9. *Cerastium nigrescens*
10. *Richea pandanifolia*

Islands

A. Japan
B. Galapagos Islands
C. Hawaii
D. Greenland
E. Chatham Island
F. Madagascar
G. Sumatra
H. Tasmania
I. Azores
J. Shetlands

QUESTION 4

Answers: page 191

QUESTION 2

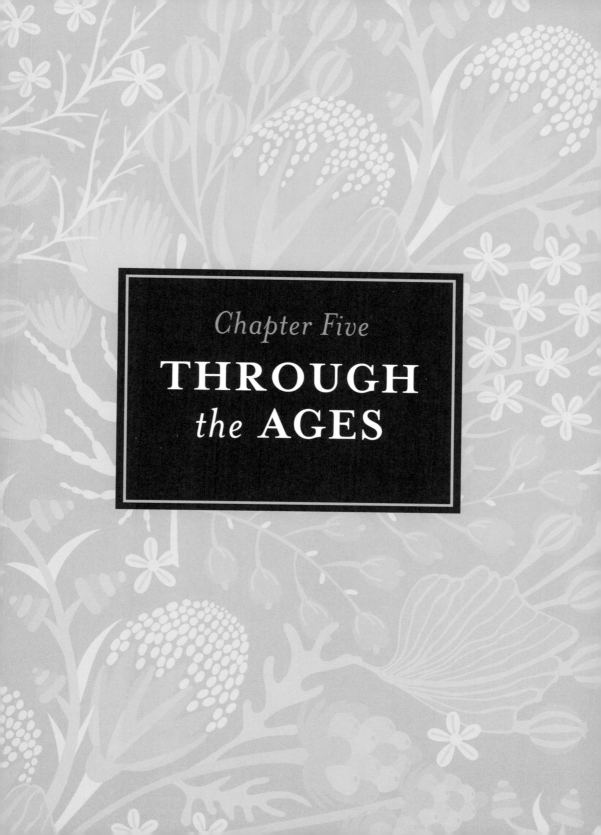

Chapter Five

THROUGH
the AGES

Mix and match: Whose garden?

Each word listed in the left-hand column is a historic gardener who either designed or is closely associated with one of the gardens on the right. Can you pair them all up?

COURTYARD IN THE ALHAMBRA, GRANADA, SPAIN

Gardeners

1. Capability Brown
2. Sôami
3. André Le Nôtre
4. Lawrence Johnston
5. Muhammad ibn-Yusuf ibn-Nash
6. Pietro Bernini
7. Shah Jahan
8. Gertrude Jekyll
9. Cyrus the Great
10. Claude Monet

Gardens

A. Giverny
B. Munstead Wood
C. Versailles
D. Hidcote Manor
E. Shalimar
F. Villa d'Este, Tivoli
G. Stowe
H. Alhambra
I. Pasargadae Persian Gardens
J. Daisen-in Zen Garden

Gardening titles

The following are some of the most influential gardening
books ever written. Can you fill in the missing words using
the words below?

1. *Complete ...*, by Nicholas Culpeper (1653)
2. *Colour in the ... Garden*, by Gertrude Jekyll (1908)
3. *The Dry ...*, by Beth Chatto (1978)
4. *The Well- ... Garden*, by Christopher Lloyd (1970)
5. *The ... Garden*, by William Robinson (1870)
6. *The Gardener's ...*, by Thomas Hill (1577)
7. *The ... Gardener*, by Anna Pavord (2011)
8. *... Plantarum*, by Carl Linnaeus (1753)
9. *... of Gardening*, by John C. Loudon (1822)
10. *Sylva, or a Discourse of ... Trees*, by John Evelyn (1664)

MISSING WORDS

A. *Forest*

B. *Species*

C. *Wild*

D. *Flower*

E. *Herbal*

F. *Labyrinth*

G. *Garden*

H. *Curious*

I. *Encyclopaedia*

J. *Tempered*

Answers: page 192

Quick quiz: Garden pioneers

Here's an opportunity to match your green-fingered skills with
your grey matter. Answer these quick-fire questions to test your
knowledge of early gardening.

1. Who is the patron saint of gardeners?

2. In a typical medieval monastery, who was responsible for the physic garden?

3. Which powerful Christian emperor who ruled much of Europe from 800 CE to 814 CE recommended that all the estates under his control should grow a specific range of plants?

4. The classic French heraldry symbol the fleur-de-lis is a stylised lily composed of three petals, but which are the two colours associated with it?

5. Over 40 English vineyards were mentioned in which important and fascinating document completed by the Norman conquerors of Britain in 1086?

6. What was the name of the garden in which Jesus is said to have been arrested prior to his trial and crucifixion, in approximately 33 CE?

7. In which Italian city was the first botanical garden established in 1545?

8. Which philosopher and statesman, credited with the development of the modern scientific method, wrote in 1625, 'God Almighty first planted a garden. And indeed, it is the purest of human pleasures.'?

9. Which one of the Seven Wonders of the World is thought to have been commissioned by King Nebuchadnezzar II?

10. Which Mediterranean plant's leaves were often carved at the top of columns in Ancient Greece?

11. What was the name of Kublai Khan's summer palace and garden, visited by Marco Polo in 1275?

12. The Humble Administrator's Garden has survived since the 16th century, but in which country is it?

Answers: page 192

QUESTION 10

Who am I?

These clues point to a famous figure in garden history. Can you work out who? Score 10 points if you solve the puzzle with one clue and deduct a point for each additional clue that you need.

1. I was born on 25 June 1799 in Scone, Perthshire, Scotland.

2. I am regarded as one of the most prolific plant collectors and most daring of all the 19th-century plant hunters.

3. I originally studied under Sir Joseph Hooker at the botanical garden of the University of Glasgow.

QUESTION 9

4. I was commissioned by the Royal Horticultural Society to collect plants in North America and sailed from Liverpool to New York in 1823 to explore the area.

5. I did, however, introduce many other plants to Britain, including flowering currants, penstemons and lupins.

6. I died in Hawaii on 12 July 1834, at the age of 35, by accidentally falling into a pit dug out to trap wild bulls. Unfortunately, there was already a bull in the pit.

7. Over 80 species of plants and animals have my surname in their scientific names.

8. I am known particularly for collecting pine trees from North America.

9. Probably the best-known tree that I introduced to the UK was *Pseudotsuga menziesii.*

10. The common name for this tree is Douglas fir, after my surname.

Mix and match: **Plant hunters**

On the left is a list of illustrious and courageous plant explorers, who often risked life and limb to discover new plants from all over the globe. On the right is a list of the countries and geographic areas they visited. Can you match the plant explorer with the places they explored or are predominantly associated with?

MYOSOTIS CAPITATA, COLLECTED
BY JOSEPH DALTON HOOKER

Plant Explorers

1. Joseph Dalton Hooker
2. Robert Brown
3. John Bartram
4. Ynes Mexia
5. Joseph Banks
6. Francis Masson
7. Louis van Houtte
8. Frank Kingdon-Ward
9. Joseph Martin

Countries and geographic areas

A. Australia
B. Canaries, Madeira, Azores, South Africa
C. Antarctica, Himalayas, Middle East, Western USA
D. Labrador, Newfoundland, South Pacific
E. Mexico, South America
F. Brazil
G. USA
H. Mauritius, Madagascar, Caribbean, South Africa
I. China, Tibet

Answers: page 192

What am I?

How many clues will it take you to discover what I am? Score 10 points if you solve the puzzle with one clue, and deduct a point for each additional clue that you need.

1. My life began in Thrupp, just outside Stroud, in Gloucestershire, England.

2. My first British patent was granted on 31 August 1830.

3. My inventor was called Edwin Beard Budding, and he also designed the adjustable spanner in 1842.

4. My inventor took his inspiration from a cloth mill.

5. I am considered by many to be the most important garden development in the history of horticultural efficiency.

6. Two of my earliest versions were sold to Regent's Park Zoological Gardens and Oxford colleges.

7. Before I was invented, it would take huge teams of men with scythes to carry out the equivalent job.

8. I am usually powered by manual force, petrol, electricity, battery or solar energy.

9. Popular modern makes of me include Hayter, Mountfield, Atco and Flymo.

10. I come in cylinder, rotary and hover types. People with larger gardens use a 'ride-on'.

Answer: page 192

Anagrams: Great garden designers

Can you unravel these anagrams of influential garden designers and landscape architects? In each case we've given you a clue to their identity.

1. egills menctél
Known for his designs of public parks in France

2. iretop ionicpar
One of the most highly regarded Italian landscape architects of the 20th century

3. pjshoe antpox
Head gardener at Chatsworth; later designed Crystal Place and cultivated the Cavendish banana

4. tugvas namnam
A successful Swiss landscape architect with a Modernist style

5. axbiter arcadewald rafrand
Her notable designs included gardens for the White House and the campuses at Yale and Princeton

6. agnan sawalk
A Polish opera singer who created the Lotusland botanical gardens at her mansion in Montecito, California

7. chidfirer guwild nov cellks
Introduced the English style of gardening to Germany

8. etpre hosepj énlen
Director General of the Royal Prussian palaces and parks in Potsdam and Berlin

9. bertroo elrub axmr
Credited with introducing Modernist landscape architecture to Brazil

10. take denimtold
Married to William Windsor, this lady co-designed the Back to Nature garden at the 2019 RHS Chelsea Flower Show

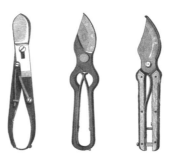

Multiple-choice: The golden age of the garden

Here are some questions to test your knowledge of
18th- and 19th-century gardening history.

1. In which country would you find these world-famous, 18th-century gardens: Chateau de Fontainebleau, Palace de Versailles, Vaux-le-Vicomte and Chateau de Chantilly?

a) *France*

b) *Belgium*

c) *The Netherlands*

d) *Luxembourg*

2. The Victoria Medal of honour (VMH) is the highest accolade that can be awarded to a person who has made an outstanding contribution to horticulture. How many recipients can hold the title at one time?

a) *24*

b) *33*

c) *64*

d) *72*

3. The Horticultural Society of London was founded in 1804 in Piccadilly, London. In what year did the society receive a Royal decree from Queen Victoria, creating the new title of the Royal Horticultural Society, or RHS?

a) *1819*

b) *1833*

c) *1856*

d) *1861*

4. Humphry Repton would present books to his prospective clients featuring his proposed garden designs. It is thought that he produced over 100 of these books. But what was their iconic colour?

a) *Blue*

b) *Red*

c) *Green*

d) *Black*

5. Many 19th-century plant collectors used a glass case invented in 1829, and named after its inventor, to keep their botanical specimens alive. What was the case called?

a) *Brownian*

b) *Smithian*

c) *Wardian*

d) *Gregian*

6. Capability Brown is possibly the most influential garden designer of all time. He is also famous for another gardening feat in 1768. What was it?

a) *Digging up a mature monkey puzzle tree in Chile and moving it to Spain*

b) *Being the first gardener to ripen a banana plant outdoors in Sussex*

c) *Planting a grapevine at Hampton Court, which is now the largest in the world*

d) *Creating the first saltwater lake in the UK in the grounds of Balmoral Castle*

Anagrams: Garden styles

There have been numerous gardening movements and styles throughout history. Can you unravel these anagrams to reveal a style or theme garden?

1. cirqueupset

2. squaredgene

3. gelshin claapdens

4. iliatan craniasense

5. rats dan frcast

6. lomfra

7. shinlge tatogec nragde

8. satiricaltun

9. nhefcr quorabe

10. dismentor

Quick quiz: **The time-travelling gardener**

Here are some quick-fire questions to see how well you know
your garden history. Green fingers on the buzzer...

1. Which plant genus is named
after Leonhart Fuchs?

2. Name the famous Tudor father
and son plant hunters who collected
curiosities from their travels
and displayed them in The Ark
in Lambeth, London.

3. The first owner of Villa Reale di
Marlia in Italy was Princess Elisa
Baciocchi. Which European leader
was her brother?

4. The first botanical garden in Sweden
was founded in 1655. What is its name?

5. What colour were the two roses
associated with the Wars of the Roses?

6. Tulip mania, with bulbs selling
for a small fortune, originated in
which European country in the early
17th century?

7. In 1673 the Worshipful Society of
Apothecaries leased a riverside plot
in London to grow medicinal plants.
What is this garden known as today?

8. John Wedgwood, son of the pottery
manufacturer Josiah Wedgwood, and
Joseph Banks were founder members of
which highly respected garden society?

9. What mythical creature, which arrived
in this country in 1867, was banned from
Chelsea Flower Show until recently?

10. At the beginning of the 20th century,
Kew Gardens was attacked, leading to the
burning of the Tea Pavilion and the
destruction of the Orchid House. Who
carried out the attack?

11. What is the Henry Doubleday Research
Association now known as?

12. Which vegetable was originally white,
yellow, purple or black but was made
orange to celebrate the accession to the
throne of William of Orange?

Answers: page 193

QUESTION 6

Multiple-choice: Garden folly

How well do you know your historic garden features? Here are a few questions to test whether you know your pergola from your pagoda.

1. In Renaissance Italy, what feature was a portico in garden architecture?

a) *An elaborate outside lavatory for the head gardener's use only*

b) *A water feature with fountains*

c) *A statue or focal point in the centre of a formal garden*

d) *A covered walkway or porch*

2. Knot gardens were popular formal designs often used in Renaissance-style gardens. They could be used to form elaborate patterns, which were often designed to be seen from above, such as from the first floor of a grand house. What type of plant is most often used to form these shapes?

a) *Buxus sempervirens*

b) *Quercus robur*

c) *Fagus sylvatica*

d) *Taxus baccata*

3. What garden or architectural feature originates from the old French word meaning throat and often can be used to describe the gurgling sound of water?

a) *Gargoyle*

b) *Gurglet*

c) *Garafe*

d) *Gurge piscine*

4. Gardens designed in the Arts and Crafts style often featured rills. What is a rill?

a) *A low, rustic wall*

b) *A parterre with island-shaped flower beds*

c) *A shallow, narrow water feature*

d) *A tree-lined avenue linking different areas of the garden*

5. Which garden design term was introduced by John Claudius Loudon in 1832 to describe a style of planting in accordance with his 'Principle of Recognition'?

a) *Picturesque*

b) *Arts and Crafts*

c) *English Landscape*

d) *Gardenesque*

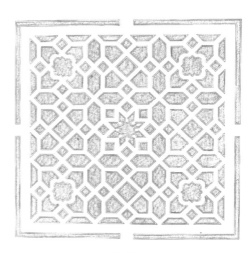

QUESTION 2

QUESTION 7

6. If your garden had a Pulham feature in it, what would this be?

a) *A rock garden*

b) *A serpentine lake*

c) *A Gothic temple*

d) *A pond for koi carp*

7. Which garden designer would often use the following features in a garden landscape: serpentine lakes, cedars of Lebanon and Gothic temples?

a) *Diarmuid Gavin*

b) *Piet Oudolf*

c) *Capability Brown*

d) *William Robinson*

8. Which historic garden feature that sounds like a laugh is a sunken ditch, cleverly designed to keep livestock out of the garden, without interrupting the sweeping views with a hedge or fence?

a) *Titter*

b) *Giggle*

c) *Ha–ha*

d) *Hee hee*

Answers: page 193

Chapter Six

GREENER GARDENING

Multiple-choice: Bird-brained

Birds are the most popular wildlife visitors to the garden. They're not always invited, but almost always welcome. How much do you know about your feathered garden friends?

1. What is the study of birds called?

a) *Ornithology*

b) *Ecology*

c) *Zoology*

d) *Featherology*

2. What type of bird will you only see in your garden at certain times of the year because it makes a regular seasonal, often extremely long, journey to another part of the world?

a) *Backpacker*

b) *Resident*

c) *Traveller*

d) *Migrant*

3. We often put out seeds out for garden birds. What are birds that feed mainly on seeds called?

a) *Frugivore*

b) *Carnivore*

c) *Herbivore*

d) *Granivore*

4. What do I study if I study birds' eggs?

a) *Shellology*

b) *Scrambology*

c) *Oology*

d) *Oviology*

5. Occasionally, you may see birds of prey in larger gardens. What is the name for this group of birds?

a) *Corvids*

b) *Raptors*

c) *Passerines*

d) *Preytors*

6. What is the flight path used in bird migration known as?

a) *Airway*

b) *Navipath*

c) *Flyroute*

d) *Flyway*

7. The family of birds *Columbidae* includes which species?

a) *Pigeons and doves*

b) *Finches*

c) *Falcons*

d) *Ducks*

8. What is the central structure in the middle of a feather called?

a) *Rachis*

b) *Barb*

c) *Bristle*

d) *Spine*

9. Birds replace and renew their feathers each year. What is this process called?

a) *Shedding*

b) *Slipping*

c) *Moulting*

d) *Feathering*

10. Charles Darwin famously researched this group of birds in the Galapagos:

a) *Blackbirds*

b) *Jackdaws*

c) *Finches*

d) *Duck-billed platypuses*

11. Why are black oil sunflower seeds better for feeding birds in the garden than striped sunflower seeds?

a) *Striped seeds are too big to swallow*

b) *Striped patterns scare off small birds*

c) *Squirrels and rats won't take the black oil ones*

d) *Black oil seeds are more nutritious*

12. What is a group of eggs in a nest called?

a) *Glitch*

b) *Clutch*

c) *Brood*

d) *Fledge*

13. What is the collective noun for crows?

a) *Raucous*

b) *Murder*

c) *Disaster*

d) *Court*

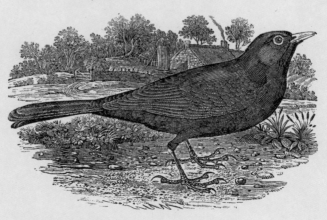

Answers: page 194

Quick quiz: Wildlife trivia

Test your wildlife knowledge by identifying the answers
from the descriptions below.

1. Gastropod often disliked by gardeners. Species include leopard, black and yellow.

2. External openings through which insects breathe.

3. Rodent with a bushy tail. There are red and grey species.

4. The number of legs that an insect has.

5. The tiny overlapping pieces of chitin on the wings of butterflies and moths.

6. Animal that lacks eyelids and, while it has no visible ears, is very good at detecting vibrations in the ground.

7. The taxonomic unit below the rank genus: a group of similar individuals that can interbreed and produce fertile offspring.

8. A close relationship between two living organisms, includes mutualism, commensalism and parasitism.

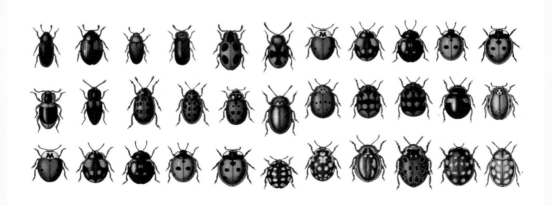

HINT: *All of the answers start with the letter 'S'.*

Mix and match: We grow together

Some plants are said to offers benefits when grown alongside certain crops, either because they offer protection against pests or attract the right pollinators. Can you match the main crop with its companion plant from the list below?

Main crops

1. Carrots
2. Runner beans
3. Tomatoes
4. Roses
5. Radishes
6. Broad beans
7. Courgettes
8. Sweetcorn
9. Cabbage
10. Strawberries

Companion plants

A. Chamomile
B. French marigolds
C. Calendula
D. Borage
E. Spring onions
F. Garlic
G. Sweet peas
H. Sunflowers
I. Summer savory
J. Mint

Solution: page 194

What am I?

Can you work out which popular, garden bird is being described here? Score 10 points if you solve the puzzle with one clue and deduct a point for each additional clue that you need.

1. I was a sacred bird to Aphrodite, the ancient Greek goddess of love.

2. I often breed and feed near people and dwellings.

3. I have a streaked brown back and a greyish underside.

4. I have a thick bill that is good for eating seeds. This is a main part of my diet, but I will also eat shoots, berries and scraps from the bird table. I feed my nestlings on invertebrates.

5. I am a sedentary bird and will disperse only a short distance from where I was born.

6. I nest in cavities and take easily to nest boxes.

7. I was recorded originally in Europe, Asia and North Africa, and have been introduced into America, Australasia, and South and East Africa.

8. My maximum recorded age is over 12 years, but my typical lifespan in the wild is three.

9. If I am male, I can easily be told apart from females due to my grey crown and black bib, which is thought to denote social status.

10. My eggs are white to blueish white with brown speckling.

Answer: page 194

The wildlife-friendly garden

Work out the missing letters below to identify features that
will help encourage wildlife in your garden.

1. W _ _ d _ _ e p _ _ d
2. B _ r _ b _ _
3. B _ g h _ t _ l
4. L _ g p _ _ e
5. _ _ l _ fl _ _ _ r m _ _ d _ _
6. D _ _ d h _ d _ _
7. B _ _ h _ _ e
8. N _ t _ ve _ _ dg _
9. N _ t _ _ e p _ t _ _
10. L _ _ f p _ _ e

Answers: page 194

Bug buddies

Gardeners often try to encourage beneficial insects into the garden for pest control or pollination, but must also avoid pests. Group the creatures listed below into the correct categories to test whether you know your friends from your enemies in the garden. (Note that some creatures may appear in more than one group.)

CREATURES

A. Green lacewing

B. Blackfly

C. Wasp

D. Ladybird

E. Solitary bee

F. Caterpillar

G. Bumblebee

H. Scale

I. Butterfly

J. Ground beetle

K. Parasitic wasp

L. Slug

M. Honey bee

N. Hoverfly

O. Thrip

P. Centipede

GROUPS

1. *Pollinators*
2. *Pest controllers*
3. *Enemies*

Planting for pollinators

Can you identify these plants, which are known
for being pollinator-friendly?

1.

2.

3.

4.

5.

6.

Answers: page 195

Grow organic

Organic gardening is more an approach to horticulture than a series of rigid rules to follow. However, there are a number of basic principles that are associated with being organic. Can you work out the missing words in the following statements to complete these principles of organic gardening?

1. Organic gardening emphasises feeding the s _ _ l rather than the plants themselves.

2. Organic gardeners aim to give plants the best possible c _ _ d _ t _ _ _ _ to ensure plants remain healthy and resistant to pests and disease.

3. Organic gardening uses _ _ t _ r _ _ methods of pest and disease control rather than chemical controls.

4. Minimising damage to the e _ _ _ _ _ n _ _ _ t is an important consideration in organic gardening.

5. Encouraging wildlife is integral to creating a healthy organic e _ _ _ y s _ _ _.

6. R _ _ y _ _ i _ _ as much as possible helps to minimise the ecological impact of an organic gardener's activities.

7. Using natural processes, such as following a no _ _ g policy, rather than working against nature, reduces the organic gardener's workload.

8. Organic gardeners do not use chemical _ _ r _ i _ _ s _ _ s, or herbicides or insecticides in their gardens as a matter of principle.

The good, the bad and the green

As a rule of thumb, bare soil should be avoided in a wildlife-friendly garden. Green manures are a popular choice for covering bare ground and improving fertility and structure, as well as attracting beneficial insects. Can you work out the common names of the plants described below, which are known to be useful green manures?

1. Y _ _ l _ _   tr _ _ o _ _
Hardy, low-growing biennial that covers ground well

2. B _ _ _ _ he _ t
Quick growing weed-suppressing plant with pollinator-attracting flowers

3. F _ _ _ d _ e _ n _
Easily grown nitrogen-fixing legume

4. M _ s _ _ r _
A wild brassica that is especially good at suppressing weeds

5. F _ _ _ g _ _ e _
A half-hardy annual that produces plenty of foliage in a short space of time

6. A _ f _ _ _ a
Deep roots help break up hard soil and cut foliage makes a good mulch

Multiple-choice: How eco-savvy are you?

Answer these multiple-choice questions to test your
eco-friendly gardening knowledge.

1. What is the name of material placed on
bare soil or around the base of plants to
suppress weeds and retain moisture?

a) *Milch*

b) *Melch*

c) *Molch*

d) *Mulch*

2. Yellow rattle *(Rhinanthus minor)* is sowed
into wildflower meadows to weaken more
vigorous grasses because...

a) *It emits a natural weedkiller*

b) *It is semi-parasitic on grasses*

c) *It is vigorous and smothers out competitors*

d) *The rattling of the plant attracts insects
that eat competing grasses*

3. Which beneficial garden visitor is shown
on the RHS pollinator-friendly logo?

a) *Beetle*

b) *Butterfly*

c) *Bat*

d) *Bee*

4. The use in many commercial composts of
which naturally occurring material, usually
extracted from bogs, is considered to be a
major environmental issue?

a) *Tar*

b) *Peat*

c) *Coir*

d) *Top soil*

5. Which of the following mammals would
be most welcome in the garden for
controlling pests?

a) *Grey squirrel*

b) *Hedgehog*

c) *Badger*

d) *Mole*

6. Permaculture is a set of principles that
emphasise what?

a) *Only planting shrubs and perennials*

b) *Not planting in straight lines*

c) *Thinking about whole natural systems
and sustainability*

d) *Removing all pests from an area for
maximum efficiency*

7. Rather than a chemical insecticide, many
green gardeners choose to use which less
damaging product in the event of a serious
pest attack?

a) *Soft soap*

b) *Washing powder*

c) *Vinegar*

d) *Coca-Cola*

8. Which natural product harvested from the
sea is often found in organic fertilisers?

a) *Ground shells*

b) *Dried jellyfish*

c) *Whale oil*

d) *Seaweed*

Answers: page 195

What are we?

Can you work out what popular garden visitor is being described below? Score 10 points if you solve the quiz with one clue and deduct a point for each additional clue that you need.

1. We can often travel up to 10km (6 miles) and at speeds of up to 24km/h (15mph) in search of plants.

2. In the wild we live in the hollows of small trees, but humans have created straw houses for us, called skeps.

3. Now we live in types of houses with names such as Langstroth, WBC, National and top bar.

4. We love to do a dance, often called a 'waggle dance'.

5. The males in our nest are called drones. They don't do any work, just mate and spend most of their time eating from our stores.

6. We are scared of smoke, as we often think it is a forest fire, which could destroy our nest.

7. The females do all the work in our home, including cleaning, feeding the young and foraging.

8. We are ruled by a lady, known as the queen, and we will defend her to the death if needed.

9. Our Latin name is *Apis mellifera*. We are a gardener's best friend, although we do have a sting in our tail.

10. Gardeners love us in the garden, not just because we pollinate lots of different crops, but also because we produce honey.

Answer: page 195

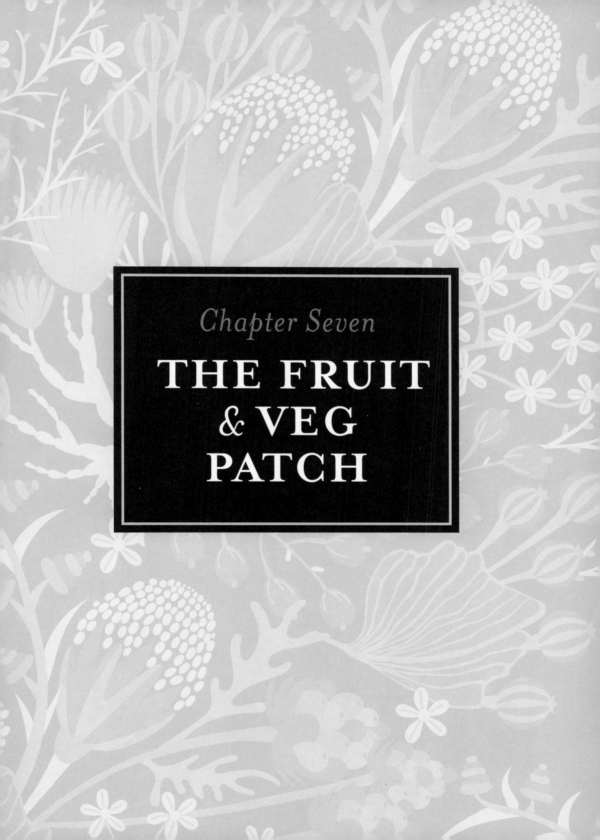

Chapter Seven

THE FRUIT & VEG PATCH

Mix and match: **Botanical beverages**

Match each drink below with the plant that is used in its production.

Drink

1. Cognac
2. Calvados
3. Gin
4. Tea
5. Rum
6. Yerba maté
7. Mudai
8. Amarula
9. Rooibos
10. Crème de cassis

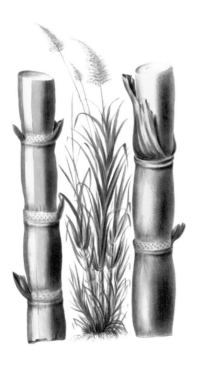

Plant

A. *Juniperus communis*
B. *Ilex paraguariensis*
C. *Vitis vinifera*
D. *Malus domestica*
E. *Camellia sinensis*
F. *Ribes nigrum*
G. *Sclerocarya birrea*
H. *Aspalathus linearis*
I. *Araucaria araucana*
J. *Saccharum officinarum*

Answers: page 196

What are we?

Can you work out which edible plant is being described
in each case below?

1. A smaller version of an onion, but rather than forming a single bulb, they form a cluster. Considered by many gourmet chefs to have a sweeter and more intense flavour.

2. A leafy vegetable, rich in iron, with a strong and sometimes bitter flavour. Made famous in *Popeye* cartoons.

3. From tropical climates, this fruit grows on the Carambola tree (*Averrhoa carambola*) and is named for the shape of its fruit.

4. Closely related to pumpkins, these popular cucurbits have winter and summer varieties.

5. Often confused with turnips, their name is similar to that given to somebody from a country in Scandinavia.

6. These popular South American tubers are susceptible to frost, so need protection. They're usually grown from slips. A cute spud!

7. A sweet red, or occasionally white or yellow, fruit. Seeds are on the outside of the skin and they're propagated by runners.

8. A culinary and aromatic herb belonging to the group of plants known as salvias. A popular savoury accompaniment to roast chicken.

HINT: *All of the answers start with the letter 'S'.*

Quick quiz: Herbal trivia

Test your knowledge of herbs with these quick-fire questions.

1. What does it mean if a plant's species name ends in *officinalis*?

2. Which four herbs are mentioned in the song 'Scarborough Fair'?

3. What leafy herb from South America is considered to be 200 times sweeter than sugar yet with no calories?

4. Which herb has popular types that include spear, apple and garden?

5. In the television programme *Fawlty Towers* what was the name of the owner of a hotel in Torquay, Devon, who shared his name with a culinary herb?

6. Name the blue-flowered herb from the mint family that cats can't get enough of.

7. The French word for dandelion is *pissenlit* — why?

8. *Isatis tinctoria, Reseda lutea* and *Potentilla erecta* are all plants grown historically for what purpose?

QUESTION 7

9. What is the name of the aromatic flower and berry that are produced from *Sambucus nigra* and used to make cordials and country wines?

10. Name the spice that is often referred to as 'poor man's saffron'?

11. Which two related edible crops are most susceptible to blight?

12. What crop has varieties that share their names with an ancient city in Israel and the shape of the world?

13. What vegetable shares part of its common name with the capital of Belgium?

14. Which member of the cabbage family has a variety that produces stems so big and sturdy that they've been used as walking sticks, particularly on the Channel Islands?

15. The Iroquois people (Native North Americans) developed a growing technique using three vegetables called the Three Sisters system. Which three vegetables were they?

QUESTION 10

Answers: page 196

Mix and match: Eat me

Match the edible crops below to the section of the plant
that is predominantly used in the kitchen.

EDIBLE CROP

1. Potato
2. Cinnamon
3. Tomato
4. Ginger
5. Broccoli
6. Cardamom
7. Fenugreek
8. Leeks
9. Saffron
10. Poppy

PARTS OF
THE PLANT

A. Tuber
B. Seed pods
C. Stigma
D. Seed
E. Rhizome
F. Bark
G. Florets
H. Stem
I. Leaves
J. Fruit

Answers: page 196

Anagrams: **Higgledy-piggledy herbs**

Can you unscramble these botanical names to reveal the herbs?
If you need a hint, the common names are at the foot of the page.

1. *hamnet saverins*

2. *galanice anarchicgale*

3. *suarul boilsin*

4. *roamsruins failsonicif*

5. *relentsopium crimpus*

6. *acridmourn viamust*

7. *mythus lagvirus*

8. *omicum alibiscum*

Multiple-choice: **Vegging out**

Test your vegetable-gardening knowledge with these
multiple-choice questions.

1. What type of vegetable can include
French, navy, kidney and broad?

a) *Cucumber*

b) *Pepper*

c) *Aubergine*

d) *Bean*

2. What word means fear of vegetables?

a) *Lacanophobia*

b) *Vegaphobia*

c) *Herbaphobia*

d) *Mulcophobia*

3. What is the name of the technique
whereby potato tubers are exposed to light
indoors prior to planting, to encourage
early shoots to form?

a) *Stratifying*

b) *Chitting*

c) *Grafting*

d) *Layering*

4. What does 'crop rotation' mean?

a) *Turning a vegetable upside down after
harvesting*

b) *Growing a different crop in a different
vegetable bed each year*

c) *Sharing a rota with others for harvesting the
crops in community gardens*

d) *Taking it in turn to only grow one crop
each season*

5. Which one of the following crops is
grown as a perennial, produces spears and
can take up to three years before its ready
for harvesting?

a) *Lettuce*

b) *Endive*

c) *Asparagus*

d) *Mizuna*

QUESTION 3

6. Which of the following is botanically a vegetable?

a) *Tomato*

b) *Courgette*

c) *Aubergine*

d) *Rhubarb*

7. What is the name of the scale used to measure the heat of chillies?

a) *Scoville*

b) *Pepperamator*

c) *Capsicumer*

d) *Brocanmiester*

8. Gardener's delight, Black Russian and Money Maker are all varieties of which fruit?

a) *Courgette*

b) *Tomato*

c) *Aubergine*

d) *Pepper*

9. What is the edible part of sweetcorn called?

a) *Kernel*

b) *Tendril*

c) *Pulse*

d) *Drupe*

10. Which parts of the amaranth plant would you usually eat?

a) *Roots and stems*

b) *Leaves and roots*

c) *Flowers and root*

d) *Leaves and seeds*

QUESTION 11

11. What type of fruit are the following: calamondin, kabosu, kumquat, meyer and ugli fruit?

a) *Plantain*

b) *Citrus*

c) *Prunus*

d) *Apple*

12. What is the offshoot of a strawberry called?

a) *Jogger*

b) *Sprinter*

c) *Trailer*

d) *Runner*

Answers: page 196

Who's who in the veg garden?

Gardeners often grow vegetables in groups with others from the same family, as they share similar growing requirements. Can you organise these crops into their groups, as you would expect to find them in a traditional kitchen garden?

GROUPS

1. *Legumes* 2. *Brassicas* 3. *Alliums* 4. *Root crops*

A. Chives

B. Runner bean

C. Cabbage

D. Borlotti

E. Skirret

F. Carrot

G. Shallots

H. Sugar snap

I. Turnip

J. Elephant garlic

K. Brussel sprout

L. Parsnip

M. Kohlrabi

N. Salsify

O. Mange tout

P. Onion

HINT: *There are four vegetables in each group.*

Multiple-choice: Fruity facts

Answer these multiple-choice questions to test your fruit-growing knowledge.

1. What type of top fruit has types known as Duke, sweet and sour?

a) *Plum*

b) *Cherry*

c) *Apple*

d) *Damson*

2. Pear trees are often grafted onto what type of fruit tree?

a) *Quince*

b) *Mulberry*

c) *Meddler*

d) *Raspberry*

3. Which of these apple rootstocks will produce the smallest tree?

a) *M25*

b) *M26*

c) *M27*

d) *MM111*

4. Blackcurrants are often grown as what type of bush?

a) *Chair bush*

b) *Bench bush*

c) *Stool bush*

d) *Sofa bush*

5. What is brown turkey?

a) *A rake with a curved neck*

b) *Slang for poultry manure*

c) *Abnormal growth on apple trees*

d) *A type of fig*

6. What is colt when found in a fruit garden?

a) *A gun–like noise machine used for scaring pigeons*

b) *A dwarfing rootstock for cherry trees*

c) *A form of nutrient–dense manure from young male horses*

d) *Grease bands placed around the trunks of trees for pest control*

Answers: page 197

What am I?

How many clues will it take you to guess what fruit or vegetable I am? Score 10 points if you solve the puzzle with one question and deduct a point for each additional question that you need.

1. I belong to the *Grossulariaceae* family.

2. I have two different species with the botanical names *Ribes uva-crispa* (European) and *Ribes hirtellum* (American).

3. In Northern England, in Victorian times, there were many clubs dedicated to growing me and where people would compete to grow the largest specimen.

4. Many of my old varieties are prone to a disease called American mildew.

5. I am a soft fruit with a similar growth habit to redcurrants and should be pruned in a similar way.

6. In gardens I often grow as fans, cordons or freestanding bushes.

7. I have over 100 varieties. Names include: 'Invicta', 'London', 'Whinham's Industry', 'Achilles' and 'Poorman'.

8. Gardeners often dread pruning me, due to my thorny branches.

9. The first part of my common name is a well-known farmyard bird.

10. I went out of favour in the 20th century due to my sharpness and hairiness, but have recently been enjoying a revival. After all, I am nobody's fool!

Answer: page 197

Mix and match: Key ingredients

Can you match each dish below with the fruit or
vegetable it is traditionally made with?

DISH

1. French fries
2. Sauerkraut
3. Moussaka
4. Houmous

5. Tarte Normande
6. Pesto
7. Guacamole
8. Marmalade

9. Dhal
10. Clafoutis
11. Tzatziki
12. Tabasco

FRUIT AND VEGETABLES

A. Cherry
B. Lentil
C. Cabbage
D. Chilli

E. Avocado
F. Aubergine
G. Chickpea
H. Apple

I. Basil
J. Cucumber
K. Potato
L. Seville orange

Answers: page 197

Fruit IDs

Can you identify the common names of the fruits pictured below?
Once you're done, put the first letter of each fruit together to
reveal the name of another bonus fruit.

1.

2.

3.

4.

5.

6.

Mix and match: Name that veg

Match the genus on the left-hand side with the correct species on the right to create the full botanical names of popular vegetables.

Genus

1. Daucus
2. Cucumis
3. Cucurbita
4. Beta
5. Apium
6. Cichorium
7. Zea
8. Armoracia
9. Pisum
10. Solanum
11. Ipomoea
12. Allium

Species

A. vulgaris
B. tuberosum
C. graveolens
D. sativum
E. sativus
F. pepo
G. rusticana
H. cepa
I. intybus
J. mays
K. carota
L. batatas

Answers: page 197

Chapter Eight

BUGS & BEASTIES

Quick quiz: Garden nightmares

Test your knowledge of garden problems with
these quick-fire questions.

1. Plants breeds that are known to be at less risk from specific pests or diseases are said to be what?

2. What name is given to a sugary liquid excreted by sap-sucking insects, which often attracts a fungus known as 'sooty mould'?

3. This curved grub with a brown head likes to chew on grass roots. What is it called?

4. What is the name of the airborne fungus that causes raised pink spots that cover tree bark and wood, and which can be fatal to woody plants?

5. Variegated shrubs and plants may sometimes start to put out pure green branches in a process known as what?

6. Which invasive plant that has been around since the time of the dinosaurs spreads by means of deep runners and is often referred to as 'horsetail'?

7. Yellow leaves are a symptom of which disorder, usually caused by nutrient shortages and common amongst acid-loving plants?

8. If your neighbour placed used grapefruit halves upside-down in their garden, which slimy pest would they be trying to trap?

9. Which pest can be controlled by a physical barrier no more than 60cm (2ft) high?

10. What is the term for an abnormal growth that a plant may produce in response to chemicals secreted by an animal or microorganism?

Mix and match: Diagnosis veg

Can you connect these plant diseases and disorders with the fruit
and vegetables they are most commonly associated with?

Plant diseases

1. Blossom end rot
2. Clubroot
3. Big bud mite
4. Blackleg
5. Green top
6. Neck rot
7. Whiptail
8. Bitter pit
9. American mildew
10. Chocolate spot

Fruit and vegetables

A. Onions
B. Cauliflower
C. Gooseberries
D. Cabbages
E. Blackcurrants
F. Carrots
G. Tomatoes
H. Apples
I. Broad beans
J. Potatoes

What am I?

Can you guess what garden pest I am from the clues below?
Score 10 points if you can solve the puzzle with one clue and
deduct a point for each additional clue that you need.

1. All adults of my species are female and can lay hundreds of eggs over a period of several months.

2. I cause the most damage during my larval stage, between autumn and spring, but less destructive signs of my activity can be seen in summer as I reach adulthood.

3. At maturity I am around 9mm (0.4in) long, a dull brown-black colour and have bent antennae.

4. I am unable to fly and I am slow-moving, so can be spotted crawling around, especially at night.

5. My eggs are sometimes confused with the slow-release fertiliser pellets in nursery-bought plants, but are actually almost too small to see.

6. My larvae are plump, white, curved and legless, and live and pupate in the soil.

7. Chemical control is available, but I am often controlled biologically with nematodes, microscopic worms that infect me with lethal bacteria.

8. Early symptoms of larval infestation of a plant are slow growth followed by wilting. Unless caught, I will kill your favourite plant.

9. I am best known as a serious pest of container and pot plants, both indoors and out, especially favouring *Heuchera* plants, succulents and polyanthus.

10. My larvae cause damage by feeding on roots and stem bases, and the tubers of cyclamen and begonia plants, while adults chew notches out of shrub leaves.

Answer: page 198

Fruit, flower, leaf, root

Can you identify the part of the plant that the following garden
pests and diseases are known to attack: fruit, flower, leaf or root?

1. **Codling moth**

2. **Eelworm**

3. **Verticillium wilt**

4. **Pigeons**

5. **Carrot fly**

6. **Capsid bug**

7. **Slugworm**

8. **Petal blight**

9. **Brown rot**

10. **Tortrix moth**

Answers: page 198

Multiple-choice: Biosphere blunders

Through the ages, certain pests and diseases have had profound impacts on ecosystems and changed the course of human history. Can you identify the right answer for each of these stories of ecological and horticultural disaster?

1. Colonists first brought rabbits to this country in 1788 for food and later for hunting purposes. Although initially the expanding numbers were not seen as a problem, within a century the population of wild rabbits had exploded, seeing the single largest recorded spread of a mammal ever, with devastating consequences for the landscape. Mild winters and a lack of natural predators have ensured that they continue to be a problem even today, and control measures include banning them as pets, introducing infectious diseases and building huge fences to keep them away from vulnerable crops. Which country has been overrun by bunnies?

a) *Jamaica*

b) *Hawaii*

c) *Australia*

d) *Argentina*

2. This microorganism caused the mass migration of over 20 per cent of one country's entire population and over a million deaths, which helped fuel a long, destructive sectarian conflict. It was a factor in a number of revolutions throughout Europe and had a profound impact on the course of human history. Preferring cool, moist environments, its effect peaked in Ireland from 1845 to 1849. An unprecedented famine resulted due to a huge proportion of the population being dependant on only one crop as their staple food. What is the microorganism?

a) *Claviceps purpurea*

b) *Phytophthora infestans*

c) *Armillaria*

d) *Erwinia amylovora*

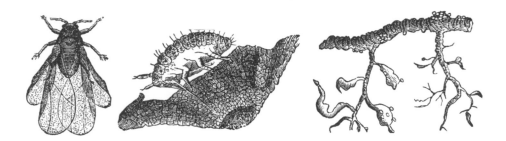

3. In the late 19th century an epidemic of aphid-like bugs almost destroyed an entire industry. Introduced from America by British botanists, *Phylloxera* attacked European species of this plant with devastating consequences, as it had no natural resistance. Transmitted from England to mainland Europe, *Phylloxera* first caused unexplainable destruction of this crop in the southern Rhône region of France before spreading rapidly throughout the continent. Within 15 years, production of Europe's finest commodity had dropped by over two-thirds. Fortunately, American plant species are somewhat more resistant, so grafting this plant onto an American rootstock has mostly solved the problem. What is the plant species?

a) *Daucus carota*

b) *Malus domestica*

c) *Triticum aestivum*

d) *Vitis vinifera*

4. Today, gardeners are facing biosecurity issues on an ever-increasing scale, as more and more plants and crops are transported around the world. But there are other, more indirect, ways that human activity may be leading to problems that will affect our survival in the future. The increasing warming of the planet means some, hitherto relatively contained, pests are thriving. One current outbreak of *Dendroctonus ponderosae*, the wood-boring pine beetle, has now killed over 13 million hectares (32 million acres) of pine wood in Canada. Rather than removing the most important element causing climate change, the forest has now become a source of it. Which element is it?

a) *Oxygen*

b) *Methane*

c) *Carbon*

d) *Nitrogen*

Answers: page 198

Most wanted line-up

Can you identify the garden villains from their pictures below?
All are found globally.

1.

2.

3.

4.

5.

6.

7.

8.

Six-letter nasties

Can you identify the missing six-letter words?

1. Powdery ...
A common problem of asters and chrysanthemums as well as various vegetables; most prevalent in warm, dry weather

2. Leaf-...
The small grub of a number of insects that tunnel through leaf tissue leaving ribbon–shaped scars

3. Lily ...
This bright–red adult and its slimy, greedy grubs can devastate the leaves and flowers of lilies and fritillaries

4. Apple ...
Tell–tale signs of this serious disease include cracked and shrinking bark and red growths in winter

5. Halo ...
A bacterium that attacks French and runner beans, causing dark leaf spots surrounded by a yellow ring

6. Pea ...
Discoloured foliage, scarring of pods and a lack of seeds inside are symptoms of an attack of these 2mm–long pests

7. ... leaf
Symptom of a fungus that invades fresh wounds of deciduous trees, the resulting toxins causing the leaf surface to separate from the leaf blade

Answers: page 198

Know your problem

Issues in the garden can take many forms, and there are few gardeners who will not come across some kind of trouble sooner or later, no matter how good they are. It is always useful to know what kind of difficulty you might be facing. Can you group the following garden problems by type?

GROUPS

1. *Pests* **2.** *Diseases* **3.** *Disorders*

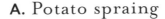

A. Potato spraing
B. Waterlogging
C. Scale
D. Larch adelgid
E. Tulip fire
F. Oedema
G. Corky scab
H. Shot hole
I. Fasciation
J. Whitefly
K. Smut
L. Mealybug

HINT: *There are four issues per group.*

Multiple-choice: **Plant plight**

The most popular garden plants are often the ones that are most susceptible to pests and diseases. How well do you know the potential problems your favourite plants may be prone to?

1. Which of the following does not affect roses?

a) *Blackfly*

b) *Rust*

c) *Blackspot*

d) *Rhizome rot*

2. Which of the following is not a problem of root vegetables?

a) *Violet root rot*

b) *Fanging*

c) *White blister*

d) *Slime flux*

3. Which one of the following will not affect the health of an apple tree?

a) *Codling moth*

b) *Winter moth*

c) *Powdery mildew*

d) *Agapanthus gall midge*

4. Which of the following is not an issue when growing fuchsias?

a) *Fuchsia gall mite*

b) *Fireblight*

c) *Red spider mite*

d) *Elephant hawk moth*

5. Which of the following will not trouble rhododendrons?

a) *Bud blast*

b) *Azalea whitefly*

c) *Clubroot*

d) *Dry bud*

Answers: page 199

Fill the blanks: Winning the battle

It might seem that our gardens and plants are under attack from all sides but we do have some weapons at our disposal to successfully wage horticultural war. Can you guess the missing words and bring hope to gardeners everywhere that some battles at least can be won?

1. A p _ _ _ _ _ _ e trap uses sex hormones to lure amorous pests looking for a mate.

2. A pest- or disease-controlling chemical that is absorbed into the plant's tissues is often referred to as s _ _ _ _ _ _ c.

3. 'P _ _ _ _ _ _ _ _ n is better than control' is a common-sense approach to modern gardening that will help avoid unnecessary environmental impact.

4. Buying seed potatoes that are c _ _ _ _ _ _ _ d should help to reduce the incidence of problematic viruses.

5. Slugs and snails appear not to like crawling over tapes made of c _ _ _ _ r.

6. Worm casts in a lawn are unsightly but not harmful, and are best swept away with a twiggy broom called a b _ _ _ m.

7. Minimise 'damping off' of seedlings by maintaining scrupulous h _ _ _ _ _ e and watering with clean tap water.

8. A simple way of preventing cutworms from destroying your brassica crop is to use cabbage c _ _ _ _ _ s.

9. Regular, consistent watering of root vegetables will prevent them from s _ _ _ _ _ _ _ g and reduce the possibility of pathogens entering through open wounds.

10. Earwigs love chewing dahlia flowers but are easily trapped by leaving upside-down f _ _ _ _ _ _ _ s stuffed with straw nearby overnight and removing them in the morning.

Answers: page 199

Anagrams: Chemical-free critter control

As the research into the negative effects of pesticides on the wider environment intensifies, gardeners are increasingly looking to less damaging methods of pest control. In some cases just encouraging beneficial animals, birds and insect predators into the garden can help. Can you unscramble the following anagrams to work out which pests are controlled by these biological weapons?

1. erraticpall
Bacillus thuringiensis (bacterium)

2. vein evilwe
Steinernema kraussei (nematode)

3. drepris time
Phytoseiulus persimilis (mite)

4. yewfilth
Encarsia formosa (wasp)

5. glus
Phasmarhabditis hermaphrodita (nematode)

6. adhips
Aphidoletes aphidomyza (midge)

7. ambleguy
Cryptolaemus montrouzieri (beetle)

8. sugfun gant
Hypoaspis miles (mite)

Answers: page 199

Lawn troubles

Can you figure out what problem, pest or disease is making
a mess of the lawn in each picture below? We've given you
the first letters.

1. L

2. F

3. W

4. F

5. R

6. F

What am I?

How many clues will it take you to figure out what plant problem I am? Score 10 points if you solve the puzzle with one clue and deduct a point for each additional clue you need.

1. I am an oomycete plant pathogen with an uncertain origin.

2. I was first reported in 1995 but may have been around before that, either unnoticed or confused with other plant diseases with similar symptoms.

3. I produce both chlamydospores (resting spores), which can survive harsh winters, and zoospores (swimming spores).

4. I was first spotted on the tree *Notholithocarpus densiflorus*, which is native to California.

5. Early identification of me is tricky, requiring laboratory testing.

6. I can be transmitted by both air and water, on the boots of human hikers, or on infected firewood or nursery plants.

7. I cause dieback and browning of leaves and branches, bleeding sap on trunks and, in susceptible species, death.

8. I am a serious problem on the West Coast of America and in Europe, having now been recorded in 16 countries.

9. Certain plant species, such as the California bay laurel (*Umbellularia californica*) and *Rhododendron ponticum*, act as hosts or 'inoculum', transmitting the disease to more susceptible species.

10. I affect oaks, although native European oaks do not seem to be susceptible.

Answer: page 199

Chapter Nine

BRANCHING OUT

To climb or not to climb

Which of the following plants *are not* climbers?

A. *Wisteria sinensis*

B. *Fatsia japonica*

C. *Parthenocissus quinquefolia*

D. *Cotinus coggygria*

E. *Clematis montana*

F. *Hydrangea petiolaris*

G. *Trachelospermum jasminoides*

H. *Vitis coignetiae*

I. *Choisya ternata*

J. *Akebia trifoliata*

HINT: *Three are not climbers.*

Colour comrades

Can you place these trees and shrubs into groups based
on the colour of their flowers?

GROUPS

1. *White* 2. *Yellow* 3. *Blue* 4. *Red*

TREES AND SHRUBS

A. *Paeonia delavayi*

B. *Crinodendron hookerianum*

C. *Embothrium coccineum*

D. *Magnolia grandiflora*

E. *Perovskia atriplicifolia*

F. *Cornus mas*

G. *Hypericum perforatum*

H. *Ceanothus impressus*

I. *Forsythia intermedia*

J. *Viburnum opulus*

K. *Yucca gloriosa*

L. *Ceratostigma willmottianum*

HINT: *There are three plants in each group.*

Quick quiz: Wooded wonders

Answer these quick-fire questions to test your knowledge of trees and shrubs. To help, we've give you the initial letters of the answers.

1. Who wrote these words: 'A rose tree stood near the entrance of the garden; the roses on it were white, but there were three gardeners at it, busily painting them red'? **LC**

2. *Acer palmatum* is better known as what? **JM**

3. Which plant hunter introduced the monkey puzzle tree to the UK? **WL**

4. What name is given to a type of ornamental, deciduous cherry with dramatic, peeling, reddish-brown bark? **PS**

5. What is the name for the phenomenon whereby the main, central stem of a tree is dominant over its laterals? **AD**

6. *Salix caprea* is better known as what? **GW**

7. What is the name of the palm with dark, fan-shaped leaves up to 1m (3.3ft) in width and best known for being one of the hardiest of its types? **TF**

8. If a tree is sold in a garden centre without being grown in a container, it is called what? **BR**

9. The Nordmann fir is an evergreen conifer that is often brought indoors in December and used as a... **CT**

10. Discovered in New South Wales, Australia, in 1994, what conifer had been thought to be extinct until then? **WP**

Mix and match: **Small but stunning**

Match the genus with the species, to reveal the names
of some of the most beautiful small trees in the world.

Genus		Species	
1.	*Cornus*	A.	*persica*
2.	*Magnolia*	B.	*pseudoacacia*
3.	*Pyrus*	C.	*coggygria*
4.	*Parrotia*	D.	*mas*
5.	*Robinia*	E.	*paniculata*
6.	*Rhus*	F.	*soulangeana*
7.	*Ligustrum*	G.	*salicifolia* 'Pendula'
8.	*Koelreuteria*	H.	*typhina*
9.	*Crataegus*	I.	*lucidum*
10.	*Cotinus*	J.	*laevigata*

Answers: page 200

Bushy botanical names

Using the clues below, can you work out the botanical names of these trees or shrubs? We have given you the length of the words and a few of the letters to help you. Once you're done, write down the first letters of each plant to reveal another popular tree.

1. _ _ pp _ _ _ _ _   rh _ _ _ _ _ _ _ _
A spiny deciduous shrub with bright orange berries and sharp thorns; associated with coastal regions

2. _ _ _ _ _ th _ _   b _ _ _ _ oo _ _ _
A dense evergreen shrub with dark leaves and fragrant clusters of tiny flowers from mid to late spring; often used to create a scented hedge

3. _ h _ d _ d _ _ _ _ _ _   p _ _ _ _ _ _ _
Considered to be an invasive form of a popular evergreen shrub

4. _ o _ _ _ f _ _ _ s
Know as southern beech, this tree is a genus of more than 20 species from the southern hemisphere

5. _ e _ _ l _ u _ _ l _ _   var.
j _ _ q _ _ _ _ _ _ _ i _
Grown for its stunning white trunk and smooth yet peeling bark, this tree makes a bold feature whether planted as a single specimen or in a group

6. _ r _ _ b _ _ y _ j _ p _ n _ _ a
An evergreen shrub with large glossy leaves, small panicles of white flowers and succulent loquat fruit

7. _ c _ c _ a d _ _ _ b _ t _
An attractive evergreen shrub, with finely divided, almost feathery foliage and fragrant yellow flowers that appear in late winter and early spring; often called mimosa

8. _ _ h _ n _ a j _ _ _ n _ _ _
A fragrant, winter-flowering, medium-sized evergreen shrub with light yellow dropping sprays of flowers and purple-black berries

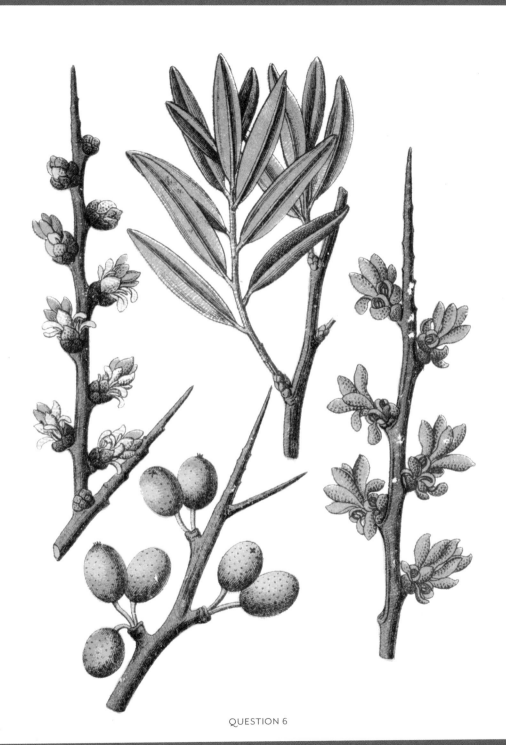

QUESTION 6

Mix and match: Animal attraction

Match the animals below with the correct words to create the
common names of some popular trees, shrubs and subshrubs.

GENUS

1. Monkey
2. Dog
3. Horse
4. Snake
5. Butterfly
6. Goose
7. Mule
8. Lion's
9. Elephant
10. Bat face

SPECIES

A. bark
B. ear
C. puzzle
D. flower
E. berry
F. tail
G. chestnut
H. wood
I. bush
J. fat

Answers: page 200

Functional flora

Can you place these trees and shrubs into the correct categories
based on what they are usually grown for?

CATEGORIES

1. *Late spring- and summer-flowering shrubs* **2.** *Colourful autumn foliage*
3. *Winter-flowering shrubs* **4.** *Winter stems* **5.** *Edible fruit*

TREES AND SHRUBS

A. *Chimonanthus praecox*

B. *Deutzia rosea*

C. *Philadelphus coronarius*

D. *Cornus sanguinea* 'Midwinter Fire'

E. *Malus domestica*

F. *Salix alba* var. *vitellina* 'Britzensis'

G. *Weigela florida*

H. *Acer palmatum*

I. *Rubus cockburnianus*

J. *Pyrus communis*

K. *Liquidambar styraciflua*

L. *Nyssa sinensis*

M. *Sarcococca humilis*

N. *Lonicera fragrantissima*

O. *Prunus armeniaca*

HINT: *There are three plants in each group.*

Multiple-choice: Tree trivia

Test your tree and shrub knowledge with these
multiple-choice questions.

1. Camellias are well-known
spring-flowering shrubs, but which one of
these predominately flowers in autumn?

a) *Camellia sasanqua*

b) *Camellia japonica*

c) *Camellia sinensis*

d) *Camellia williamsii*

2. Hydrangea flowerheads can be
affected by the acidity of the soil.
What colour can it turn the flowers?

a) *Pink*

b) *Green*

c) *Yellow*

d) *Blue*

3. The gympie gympie tree from Australia
and Indonesia is famous for what amazing
fact?

a) *Being the world's tallest tree*

b) *Having the most painful sting in the world*

c) *Having the largest flowerheads in the world*

d) *Having the densest wood in the world*

4. Which genus of trees
does a sycamore belong to?

a) *Acer*

b) *Betula*

c) *Malus*

d) *Prunus*

5. The world's tallest tree is called
Hyperion and grows in California. It was
discovered in 2006 and is 115.7m (379.7ft)
tall. What type of tree is it?

a) *Metasequoia glyptostroboides*

b) *Sequoia sempervirens*

c) *Sequoiadendron giganteum*

d) *Picea sitchensis*

QUESTION 4

6. In Japan, Sakura is the celebration of what phenomenon?

a) *The rice crop being ready for harvesting for wine*

b) *Cherry tree blossom*

c) *The autumn foliage of Japanese maples*

d) *The first azalea blooms appearing in spring*

7. *Davidia involucrata* is often referred to as the handkerchief tree, but why?

a) *The pollen from the flowers makes people sneeze*

b) *The flower bracts look like handkerchiefs*

c) *The local people wept when its seed was first collected and taken abroad*

d) *The leaves are used in China in the manufacturing of handkerchiefs*

8. *Acer griseum* is a popular garden tree because it has...

a) *Ornamental, coppery-coloured, peeling bark*

b) *Grey (gris) flowers as large as dinner plates*

c) *A small, compact habit at only 1m (3.3ft) high*

d) *Evergreen foliage that forms a dense canopy for screening*

9. What is *Fraxinus excelsior* better known as?

a) *English oak*

b) *German birch*

c) *Irish yew*

d) *European ash*

10. *Laurus nobilis* is popular among chefs because of its...

a) *Spicy tap root*

b) *Edible flowers*

c) *Aromatic leaves*

d) *Truffles that form around the roots*

QUESTION 1

11. Which of the following magnolias is evergreen?

a) *Magnolia grandiflora*

b) *Magnolia stellata*

c) *Magnolia liliiflora*

d) *Magnolia wilsonii*

12. *Dicksonia antarctica* is a type of...

a) *Bamboo*

b) *Epiphyte*

c) *Tree fern*

d) *Conifer*

Answers: page 201

Anagrams: Confused conifers

Can you unravel the anagrams below to work out the botanical names of these conifers? To help you out, we've also given you their common names.

1. *basei darings*
(Grand fir)

2. *asiaemtoque poretdybologists*
(Dawn redwood)

3. *iambicroot saucedsat*
(Siberian cypress)

4. *hajut lcapita*
(Western red cedar)

5. *aimdotux duchtismi*
(Bald cypress)

6. *injuresup sonicmum*
(Juniper)

7. *acamerapsyhic
aliasannow*
(Lawson cypress)

8. *astux acabcat*
(English yew)

What am I?

How many clues will it take you to work out who I am?
Score 10 points if you solve the puzzle with one clue and deduct
a point for each additional clue that you need.

1. I am a type of deciduous tree growing up to 12m (39ft) high.

2. I belong to the *Moraceae* family and I am originally native to southwestern Asia.

3. Vincent van Gogh featured me in one of his paintings, which he painted while staying in an asylum, and named the painting after me.

4. I am mainly planted in gardens for my fruit, but I am also regarded for my ornamental qualities, attractive trunk, and serrated, lobed leaves.

5. I was planted up in large country houses in the UK as it was hoped I could support silkworms for the silk industry, but this proved not to be the case.

6. There is, however, a white version of me that does support silkworms.

7. There is also a red-fruiting version of me.

8. My fruit is dark purple, almost black, when ripe and up to 3cm (1.2in) long.

9. My fruit is a similar shape to a raspberry.

10. There is a famous nursery rhyme about me: 'Here We Go Round the ... Bush'.

Answer: page 201

What type?

Organise the plants below into the correct categories depending
on whether they are climbers, large trees or shrubs.

CATEGORIES

1. *Climbers* **2.** *Large trees* **3.** *Shrubs*

PLANTS

A. *Aristolochia elegans*

B. *Lavandula angustifolia*

C. *Fagus sylvatica*

D. *Passiflora edulis*

E. *Larix occidentalis*

F. *Daphne bholua*

G. *Hedera helix*

H. *Quercus robur*

I. *Rosa 'Zéphirine Drouhin'*

J. *Desfontainia spinosa*

K. *Calluna vulgaris*

L. *Acer saccharinum*

HINT: *There are four plants in each group.*

Literary trees

Work out the missing trees below to complete the titles of some famous works of literature.

1. *The Wind in the* ... , by Kenneth Grahame

2. *The Children of* ... *Tree Farm,* by Enid Blyton

3. ... *Street,* by Maeve Binchy

4. *Children of the* ... *Tree,* by Sahar Delijani

5. *Under the* ... *Tree,* by Thomas Hardy

6. *Sad* ... , by Agatha Christie

7. ... *Valley,* by Holly Throsby

8. *The* ... *Tree,* by Mary Stewart

9. *And to Think That I Saw It on* ... *Street,* Dr. Seuss

10. *Under the* ... *Tree,* by Julie Stiegemeyer

Chapter Ten

THE FLOWERBED

Mix and match: Flora and fauna

Match the animals below with the correct words to create the
common names of some perennials, annuals and bulbs. To help
you, we've included the botanical name in brackets.

Animals

1. Foxtail (*Eremurus* spp.)
2. Wolf's (*Aconitum lycotonum*)
3. Buffalo (*Buchloe dactyloides*)
4. Cat (*Nepeta faassenii*)
5. Bee (*Ophrys apifera*)
6. Kangaroo (*Anigozanthos flavidus*)
7. Toad (*Linaria purpurea*)
8. Bear's (*Acanthus spinosus*)
9. Cow (*Primula veris*)
10. Worm (*Artemesia*)

Words

A. breeches
B. bane
C. mint
D. orchid
E. lily
F. flax
G. slip
H. paw
I. wood
J. grass

Know your leaves

Can you identify the plants listed below from these pictures
of their foliage?

PLANTS

A. Lupin

B. Hosta

C. Acanthus

D. Sage

E. Heuchera

F. Delphinium

G. Peony

H. Gunnera

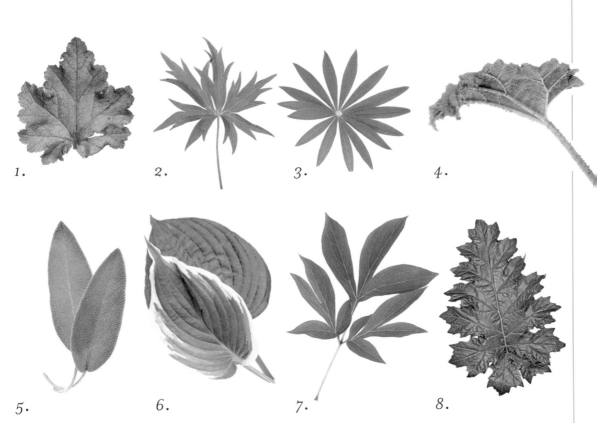

1.

2.

3.

4.

5.

6.

7.

8.

Answers: page 202

Quick quiz: Bedding beauties

Answer these quick-fire questions to test your
horticultural knowledge of perennials, annuals and bulbs.

1. What is the name of a popular garden flower from the onion family that often has large purple, globe-shaped flowerheads?

2. What connects tagetes and calendulas?

3. Who wrote the lines, 'When all at once I saw a crowd, A host, of golden daffodils'?

4. Which flowering plant connects the following words: Madonna, Easter, water, day, tiger?

5. What plants do galanthophiles collect?

6. What is the name of the flower that commemorates those who died in combat, especially in the First World War?

7. What is *Fragaria × ananassa* better known as?

8. Which popular bulb flower includes types such as trumpet, jonquilla, poeticus tazetta, split corona, triandrus, large cupped and miniature?

9. Which annual produces translucent, round, papery seed pods, which are often dried for decoration?

10. What bulb looks like a crocus but flowers in autumn?

11. Foxgloves and wallflowers are often called biennials. What does this mean?

12. Which cottage garden plant has thin, silver-grey evergreen leaves and many-petalled flowers, often with a spicy clove scent?

13. Which epiphytic species is characteristic of the swamps in the southern United States of America and drapes itself over trees?

14. 'Spencer' and 'Grandiflora' are cultivar families of which popular annual?

15. What plant, from the *Brassicaceae* family, has been used for centuries to produce a blue dye?

16. *Matteuccia struthiopteris*, a fern that resembles a shuttlecock, prefers what kind of conditions?

Answers: page 202

QUESTION 10

What type of plant?

Can you organise the plants below into the correct categories?

CATEGORIES

1. *Bulbs* 2. *Ornamental grasses*
3. *Herbaceous perennials*
4. *Annuals or tender perennials*

PLANTS

A. *Festuca glauca*
B. *Galanthus nivalis*
C. *Cosmos bipinnatus*
D. *Cortaderia selloana*
E. *Tulipa* spp.
F. *Tropaeolum majus*
G. *Pennisetum villosum*
H. *Anemone × hybrida*

I. *Echinacea purpurea*
J. *Clarkia amoena*
K. *Hyacinthus orientalis*
L. *Delphinium elatum*
M. *Stipa tenuissima*
N. *Narcissus pseudonarcissus*
O. *Hosta sieboldii*
P. *Lathyrus odoratus*

HINT: *There are four plants in each group.*

Novel plants

Identify the missing plants to complete the book titles below.

1. *The Catcher in the ...* , by J. D. Salinger

2. *The Black ...* , by Alexandre Dumas

3. *The Name of the ...* , by Umberto Eco

4. *Driving Miss ...* , by Alfred Uhry

5. *... Baby*, by Ira Levin

6. *The Scarlet ...* , by Emmuska Orczy

7. *... -Head Mayzie*, by Dr. Seuss

8. *The Lady of the ...* , by Alexander Dumas

9. *... Wine*, by Ray Bradbury

10. *The ... of the Valley*, by Honoré de Balzac

Answers: page 202

Multiple-choice: **Plant peculiarities**

Answer these multiple-choice questions to test your gardening knowledge.

1. What is *Limnanthes douglasii* commonly known as?

a) *Fried egg plant*

b) *Poached egg plant*

c) *Boiled egg plant*

d) *Scrambled egg plant*

2. Which of the following is not a bulb?

a) *Muscari armeniacum* (Armenian grape hyacinth)

b) *Scilla siberica* (Siberian squill)

c) *Begonia semperflorens* (wax begonia)

d) *Nerine bowdenii* (Guernsey lily)

3. Flowers often have extra markings that are visible to bees but not humans. Which part of the light spectrum are bees seeing that humans can't?

a) *Ultraviolet*

b) *Infrared*

c) *Magenta*

d) *Violet*

4. Which of the following is a tree and not a herbaceous plant?

a) *Alchemilla mollis*

b) *Betula utilis*

c) *Gypsophila paniculata*

d) *Taraxacum officinale*

5. Which of these plants does not have a blue flower?

a) *Meconopsis betonicifolia*

b) *Hyacinthoides non-scripta*

c) *Vinca minor*

d) *Narcissus pseudonarcissus*

QUESTION 5

6. Which of the following plants is not a succulent?

a) *Aeonium arboreum*

b) *Euphorbia milii* (crown of thorns)

c) *Hoya carnosa* (wax flower)

d) *Euphorbia epithymoides*

7. How many true species of hellebore are currently recognised?

a) 5

b) 17

c) 93

d) 22

8. *Heliotropium arborescens*, a tender perennial shrub often grown as an annual, is said to smell like which delicious dessert?

a) *Rhubarb and custard*

b) *Vanilla cheesecake*

c) *Turkish delight*

d) *Cherry pie*

9. Which of the following is not a scented geranium?

a) *Pelargonium tomentosum*

b) *Pelargonium 'Attar of Roses'*

c) *Pelargonium 'Old Spice'*

d) *Pelargonium grandiflorum*

QUESTION 11

10. In recent years, *Impatiens walleriana*, the popular bedding busy lizzie, has been the subject of a widespread disease. What is the name of the disease?

a) *Impatiens downy mildew*

b) *Impatiens rust*

c) *Phytophthora ramorum*

d) *Impatiens root rot*

11. *Mimosa pudica*, the sensitive plant, is an oddity known for what remarkable ability?

a) *It never grows more than 10cm (4in) tall*

b) *Its flowers face downwards*

c) *Its leaves fold and droop when touched*

d) *It dies when exposed to too much sunlight*

Guess the plant

Can you identify the plants from the clues below? We've revealed
part of the name to help you. Once you've finished, put the first
letters of each word together to reveal the name of another
popular garden plant.

1. _ st _ _
*One of the most popular plants in mid- to late-flowering herbaceous borders,
and whose group includes Michaelmas daisies*

2. _ h _ y _ _ n _ h _ _ _ _
*Sometimes called mums; later-flowering,
popular cut flower from the Asteraceae family*

3. _ o _ t _
A low growing plant with broad foliage; loved by slugs

4. _ ri _
*Popular types include bearded and flag;
also a woman's name*

5. _ _ t _ y _ us
A sweet pea with scented annual and perennial types

6. _ e _ c _ j _ m
A bigger version of a snowdrop — a snowflake

7. _ ch _ n _ c _ _
Cone flower; said to improve the immune system

8. _ m _ ry _ _ _ s
The belladonna lily

What am I?

How many clues will it take you to guess what plant I am?
Score 10 points if you solve the puzzle with one clue and deduct
a point for each additional clue you need.

1. I originate from America and was domesticated about 1,000 BCE. I was spread to Europe by the Spanish conquistadors in the 1500s.

2. I cover an area of nearly 700,000 hectares (1.7 million acres) in the United States alone.

3. My large flowerheads are actually made up of tiny individual flowers, sometimes as many as 2,000.

4. I'm a popular hardy annual and I am often seen on both allotments and in cut flower borders.

5. My seeds are a popular food source for garden birds.

6. My seeds can also be processed into cooking oil.

7. The French name for me is *tournesol*, meaning 'in turn with the sun'. This is because my developing flowerheads track the sun as it moves across the sky, a behaviour known as heliotropism.

8. Varieties of me include 'Russian Giant' and 'Giant Yellow'.

9. Children love growing me, and often compete to grow the tallest plant. The world record for the tallest specimen, grown by Hans-Peter Schiffer in Germany in 2014, was 9.17m (30ft).

10. My botanical name is *Helianthus*, which comes from the Greek words *helios*, meaning 'sun', and *anthos*, for flower'.

Answer: page 203

Colour categories

Can you categorise these popular herbaceous perennials based on the colour of their flowers?

GROUPS

1. *Yellow*
2. *Black*
3. *Red*
4. *Blue*

PLANTS

A. *Dahlia* 'Bishop of Llandaff'

B. *Centaurea montana*

C. *Crocosmia* 'Lucifer'

D. *Primula vulgaris*

E. *Digitalis lutea*

F. *Perovskia atriplicifolia*

G. *Tulipa* 'Queen of Night'

H. *Viola* 'Molly Sanderson'

I. *Iris* 'Before the Storm'

J. *Papaver rhoeas*

K. *Hyacinthoides non-scripta*

L. *Narcissus* 'Tête-à-tête'

HINT: *There are three plants in each group.*

Anagrams: **Flowerbed favourites**

Can you unscramble the anagrams below to reveal
the names of popular garden plants?

1. **omenspent**

2. **rates**

3. **sayid**

4. **litup**

5. **liveto**

6. **apaganshut**

7. **nazini**

8. **hadail**

Mix and match: **Garden heroes**

See if you can pair up the genus names with the species names
below, to give the botanical names of well-known garden plants.
To help you, we've kept the common name with the species.

GENUS

1. *Eschscholzia*
2. *Campanula*
3. *Achillea*
4. *Digitalis*
5. *Foeniculum*
6. *Fritillaria*
7. *Lilium*
8. *Melianthus*
9. *Phormium*
10. *Salvia*
11. *Stachys*
12. *Strelitzia*

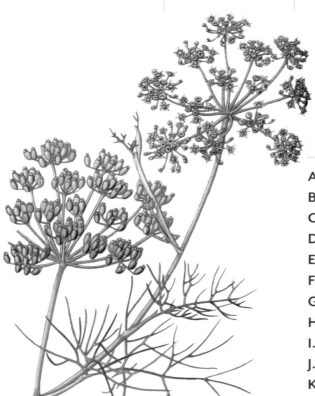

SPECIES

A. *elegans* (pineapple sage)
B. *imperialis* (Crown imperial)
C. *byzantina* (lamb's ears)
D. *tenax* (New Zealand flax)
E. *latifolia* (giant bellflower)
F. *purpurea* (foxglove)
G. *vulgare* (fennel)
H. *tigrinum* (tiger lily)
I. *major* (honey bush)
J. *californica* (California poppy)
K. *reginae* (bird of paradise)
L. *millefolium* (yarrow)

Picture perfect

Can you identify these six plants from their pictures?
Just the genus name is needed and we've given you the number
of letters in each name.

1. - - - - - -

2. - - - - -

3. - - - - - - - - - - -

4. - - - - - - - - -

5. - - - - -

6. - - - - - - -

HINT: *All the names begin with the letter 'S'.*

Chapter Eleven

BACK *to* BASICS

Where in the garden?

Can you identify the different garden features or areas that are
shown in the pictures below? We've given you the different areas
to choose from in the box on the right.

1.

2.

3.

4.

5.

6.

GARDEN AREAS

A. Compost heap
B. Raised bed
C. Greenhouse
D. Potting shed

E. Knot garden
F. Woodland garden
G. Kitchen garden
H. Mixed border

I. Water feature
J. Hanging basket
K. Green roof
L. Herbaceous border

7.

8.

9.

10.

11.

12.

Answers: page 204

Weeding worries

Can you put these weeds into the correct categories
based on whether they're perennial or annual?

GROUPS

1. *Perennial*
2. *Annual*

PLANTS

A. Groundsel
(*Senecio vulgaris*)

B. Bramble
(*Rubus fruticosus*)

C. Annual meadow grass
(*Poa annua*)

D. Hairy bittercress
(*Cardamine hirsuta*)

E. Chickweed
(*Stellaria media*)

F. Bindweed
(*Convolvulus arvensis*)

G. Stinging nettle
(*Urtica dioica*)

H. Dandelion
(*Taraxacum officinale*)

I. Fat hen
(*Chenopodium album*)

J. Ground elder
(*Aegopodium podagraria*)

Answers: page 204

Multiple-choice: Green, green grass

Answer these multiple-choice questions to test how
much you know about lawn maintenance.

1. Which of the following plants isn't
a weed usually found in the lawn?

a) *Dandelion*

b) *Yucca*

c) *Daisy*

d) *Yarrow*

2. Using a fork to spike holes in
a lawn is known as what?

a) *Aeration*

b) *Holeation*

c) *Spikation*

d) *Forkation*

3. What is the name of a traditional
hand-held implement for knocking the
moisture off blades of grass?

a) *Twitch*

b) *Snitch*

c) *Switch*

d) *Litch*

4. A vigorous scratching technique, used
on the surface of the lawn to remove dead
grass and relieve congestion of the grass
blades, is called what?

a) *Stratisfication*

b) *Scratchification*

c) *Scrapification*

d) *Scarification*

5. A type of broom made from a stout pole
with twigs attached to one end, used by
gardeners to sweep top dressing into the
lawn is called a...

a) *Besom*

b) *Bristler*

c) *Birchhead*

d) *Brosweep*

6. Which explanation below best describes
thatch in a lawn?

a) *A fungal turf disease spread by
a type of nematode*

b) *Dead and decaying grass and other organic
matter at the base of grass plants*

c) *Worm casts left on the surface of the lawn*

d) *Burnt patch on the lawn caused by sun scorch
and drought*

From the tool shed

Can you identify these items used for garden maintenance? We've given you the first letters of the words that make up their names.

1. HM

2. ES

3. LL

4. W

5. BC

6. LB

7. GF

8. DS

Answers: page 204

Put your finger on it

Can you work out what techniques are being used in the images below?
To help you, we've given you the first letters of the words that
make up their names.

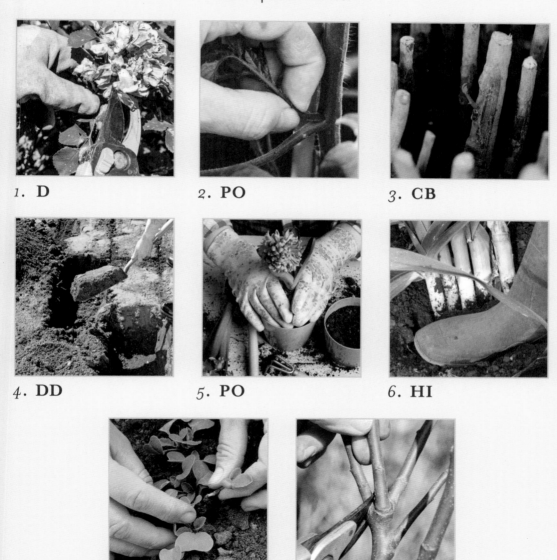

1. **D**

2. **PO**

3. **CB**

4. **DD**

5. **PO**

6. **HI**

7. **TO**

8. **P**

Answers: page 204

Fill the blanks: New life

Identify the missing letters below to reveal different methods of propagation.

1. D _ v _ s _ _ n

2. H _ _ d _ _ d c _ _ t _ _ _

3. H _ _ l c _ _ t _ g

4. M _ c _ _ p _ _ _ g _ ti _ _

5. S _ w _ _ _

6. W _ _ _ and t _ _ g _ _

7. S _ f _ w _ _ d c _ tt _ _ _

8. S _ m _ -r _ _ e c _ _ t _ _ g

9. L _ y _ r _ _ g

10. T _ _ n s _ _ l _ _ _

Shapely shrubs and trees

Can you identify the type of pruning or training system from the images below?

TYPES OF PRUNNING

A. *Pollard* **B.** *Fan* **C.** *Pleached* **D.** *Espalier* **E.** *Cordon* **F.** *Coppice*

1.

2.

3.

4.

5.

6.

Multiple-choice : **Terminology test**

Answer these multiple-choice questions to test your knowledge
of garden terminology and techniques.

1. What are the two main types of
secateurs called?

a) *Bypass and anvil*

b) *Cutters and choppers*

c) *Loppers and croppers*

d) *Snippers and tippers*

2. Renovating an old, neglected tree that
hasn't been pruned for years is known as
what?

a) *Superfluous pruning*

b) *Restorative pruning*

c) *Nostalgic pruning*

d) *Retrospective pruning*

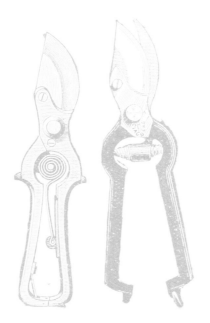

3. Gardeners often use a technique on
fruit trees to encourage a shoot to form
either just above or below a shoot. What is
the name of this technique?

a) *Bruising and breaking*

b) *Splitting and scratching*

c) *Cracking and clicking*

d) *Nicking and notching*

4. What is the modified Lorrette system?

a) *A method of venting a cold frame*

b) *A growing structure for climbing plants*

c) *A method for late-summer pruning of fruit trees*

d) *A method of irrigation using gravity on a
natural slope*

5. What is a scion stick?

a) *A rogue sucker from raspberries and other
hybrid berries*

b) *A stick used to measure the correct planting depth
for a tree*

c) *A shoot for grafting onto a rootstock*

d) *A pruning implement with an extended handle for
extra height*

6. Which of the following is the name of a
technique used to get an early crop?

a) *Compelling*

b) *Forcing*

c) *Pressuring*

d) *Coercing*

7. 'Cloche' comes from the French word for bell. What is a cloche used for in the horticultural world?

a) *A bell used in Victorian walled gardens to announce lunchtime*

b) *A bell-shaped flowerbed*

c) *A French pruning technique to shape shrubs into bell shapes*

d) *A bell-shaped cover placed over plants for protection*

8. What is cloud pruning?

a) *Shaping bushes into cloud shapes*

b) *Pruning all branches so they face upwards towards the clouds*

c) *Pruning bushes with a high, dense canopy to provide shelter from the rain*

d) *Pruning while listening to music held on a cloud*

9. What is lasagne planting?

a) *Adding pasta to a compost heap as a compost accelerator*

b) *An 19th-century Italian tradition of providing lunch for the gardeners*

c) *Building up layers of different compost materials in a bed*

d) *A method of creating layers of plants of different heights in mixed borders*

10. What is keyhole gardening?

a) *A bed with planting holes or alcoves for key shrubs in mixed borders*

b) *A type of water garden with a keyhole-shaped pond*

c) *A keyhole-shaped raised bed with a compost heap in the middle*

d) *Using a large key-shaped digging tool to dig out holes*

11. Hydroponics is gardening without providing what for the plants?

a) *Water*

b) *Soil*

c) *Oxygen*

d) *Fertiliser*

12. What is Hügelkultur?

a) *A bacterial culture added to compost heaps*

b) *A type of no-dig raised bed*

c) *A compost mix using perlite and organic moss*

d) *A fungal disease that affects seedlings*

Answers: pages 204–5

Complete your own A to Z glossary

Identify the missing words below to complete this comprehensive
A-to-Z glossary of gardening terms.

A ... – The junction between a branch and a sideshoot or a leaf stalk
that grows from it

B ... – Withholding light from the leaves of certain crops to soften
them and improve the taste

C ... – A structure made of soil and straw used to store some
vegetable crops and prevent frost damage

D ... d... – Wetting the floors and shelves, rather than the plants, in
a glasshouse, to increase humidity

E ... – A technical term for seedlings and plants that have not
received enough light; causes long, skinny stems and pale foliage

F ... – A description of perfect soil: crumbly and easy to dig – every
gardener's dream!

G ... – The artificial joining of one plant to another;
can also mean hard work

H ... o ... – Gradually introducing seedlings raised under cover to
unprotected conditions, often in a cold frame

I ... – The technical term for watering, mostly used when talking
about sprinkler systems or other mechanical methods

J ... I... – A formula for specific types of potting compost, named
after the institute that developed them

K ... g ... – A formal pattern of plants and
hedges dating back to the Tudor period

Complete your own A to Z glossary

L ... m ... — Decomposed leaves used in potting compost or as a soil improver

M ... — Fungi that live in soil and have a beneficial relationship with plants

N ... — The sugary syrup that flowers produce to attract pollinators

O ... — A plant introduced into ponds to improve the oxygen content of the water

P ... o ... — Transferring seedlings once germinated to a new position or container where they have space to grow

Q ... r ... — A flower with petals arranged in four equal sections, commonly associated with roses

R ... s ... — The area below a fence or wall which is sheltered from weather compared to more open ground

S ... — A shoot that develops below ground or under the union of a graft

T ... — The intricate art of clipping trees and shrubs into a specific shape

U ... — Planting low-growing plants beneath taller ones

V ... — Lightweight granules used when propagating or potting to improve structure and retain water

W ... b ... — A container for collecting rainwater

X ... — A botanical term, derived from Greek, for a plant that needs very little water, such as a cactus or succulent

Y ... — A period of time that dictates the garden activity calendar, due to inevitable seasonal changes in light and weather

Z ... — The term for infectious diseases, such as anthrax or toxoplasmosis, that may be transmitted from animals to humans, through infected soil or manures

Answers: page 205

ANSWERS

Answers
Chapter One: Know Your Plants

Puzzle 1: *What am I?*
Banana

Puzzle 2: *Plant portraits*
1. *Trillium*; **2.** *Allium*; **3.** *Camellia*;
4. *Crocus*; **5.** *Acer*; **6.** *Tacca*

Puzzle 3: *The A to Z of plants*

Agapanthus	*Nandina*
Bergenia	*Ophiopogon*
Cordyline	*Paeonia*
Digitalis	*Quercus*
Euphorbia	*Raphanus*
Fuchsia	*Stewartia*
Griselinia	*Taxus*
Hedera	*Ulmus*
Ilex	*Viburnum*
Juniperus	*Woodwardia*
Kerria	*Xerophyllum*
Lonicera	*Yucca*
Mahonia	*Zelkova*

Puzzle 4: *Happy families*
1. Rosaceae – **E. N.** Apple / Cotoneaster
2. Ericaceae – **F. P.** Bilberry / Heather
3. Lamiaceae – **B. K.** Mint / *Coleus*
4. Asteraceae – **A. J.** Lettuce / Chrysanthemum
5. Iridaceae – **H. O.** Crocus / *Gladiolus*
6. Liliaceae – **D. L.** Chives / Aloe
7. Brassicaceae – **C. I.** *Alyssum* / Oil seed rape
8. Primulaceae – **G. M.** Primrose / Cyclamen

Puzzle 5: *Odd one out*
1. **c)** *Penstemon*; **2. b)** *Edgeworthia*;
3. a) *Acer*; **4. d)** *Clematis montana*;
5. d) Sweet potato; **6. a)** *Dianthus*

Puzzle 6: *What am I?*
Wisteria

Puzzle 7: *Anagrams: Cucurbits*
1. Melon; **2.** Cucumber; **3.** Squash;
4. Pumpkin; **5.** Courgette; **6.** Marrow;
7. Gherkin; **8.** Watermelon

Puzzle 8: *Quick quiz: Green groupings*

1. *Rosaceae*; **2.** *Sapindaceae* (family) *Acer* (genus) *palmatum* (species) 'Sango kaku' (cultivar); **3.** *Coffea* (coffee); **4.** Peas/beans; **5.** *Asteraceae* (about 24,000 species), *Orchidaceae* (about 20,000 species), *Fabaceae* (about 18,000 species); **6.** *Nyssa*; **7.** *Salix* (willow); **8.** *Magnolioideae* and *Liriodendroidae*; **9.** Grass/bamboo; **10.** *Camellia* (*sinensis*); **11.** Olive; **12.** Cork; **13.** Agave; **14.** The *Moraceae* (mulberry) family; **15.** *Ranunculaceae*

Puzzle 9: *What am I?*

Japanese knotweed (*Fallopia japonica*)

Puzzle 10: *Plant IDs*

1. Oxeye daisy (*Leucanthemum vulgare*); **2.** Sunflower (*Helianthus*); **3.** Yarrow (*Achillea*); **4.** Dandelion (*Taraxacum*); **5.** Cornflower (*Centaurea cyanus*); **6.** Cone flower (*Echinacea*)

Answers
Chapter Two: Under the Microscope

Puzzle 11: *Colour clues*

1. **C**. *Lutea* – yellow; **2. A**. *Carneus* – pale pink; **3. F**. *Caerulae* – blue; **4. E**. *Sanguinea* – blood red; **5. G**. *Argenteus* – silver; **6. H**. *Viridis* – green; **7. B**. *Alba* – white; **8. D**. *Coccineus* – scarlet

Puzzle 12: *The language of leaves*

1. **E**. *Microphylla* (small leaves);
2. **C**. *Rotundifolia* (round leaves);
3. **A**. *Aquifolius* – spiny leaves;
4. **F**. *Cordate* – heart-shaped leaves;
5. **H**. *Longifolia* – long leaves;
6. **B**. *Palmate* – hand-shaped leaves;
7. **D**. *Pinnata* – compound leaves;
8. **G**. *Quercifolia* – oak-shaped leaves

Puzzle 13: *Mix and match: Location, location, location*

1. **C**. *Palustris* – Marshes or wetlands;
2. **J**. *Maritime* – Coasts; **3. G**. *Hortensis* – Gardens; **4. B**. *Insularis* – Islands;
5. **I**. *Riparius* – Riverbanks; **6. F**. *Saxatilis* – Rocks; **7. H**. *Campestris* – Fields;
8. **A**. *Montana* – Mountains; **9. D**. *Muralis* – Walls; **10. E**. *Sylvestris* – Forests

Puzzle 14: *Anagrams: Subterranean structures*

1. Fibrous; **2.** Tap; **3.** Rhizome;
4. Tuber; **5.** Bulb; **6.** Stolon; **7.** Corm;
8. Adventitious

Puzzle 15: *Mix and match: The global garden*

1. **I**. *Sinensis* – China; **2. E**. *Aethiopium* – Africa; **3. B**. *Helveticus* – Switzerland;
4. **H**. *Hispanicus* – Spain; **5. J**. *Gallicus* – France; **6. C**. *Cambrica* – Wales;
7. **D**. *Lusitanica* – Portugal; **8. G**. *Himalaica* – Himalayas; **9. F**. *Graeca* – Greece;
10. **A**. *Japonica* – Japan

Page 16: *Multiple-choice: What's in a name?*

1. **c)** Sleep; **2. b)** Stickiness; **3. d)** It is scented; **4. a)** North; **5. b)** Part of the plant is edible; **6. c)** Climbing

Puzzle 17: *The answer lies in the soil*

1. **E**. Sandy soil; **2. B**. Peat soil;
3. **F**. Clay soil; **4. A**. Chalky soil;
5. **D**. Loam soil; **6. C**. Silt soil

Puzzle 18: *Multiple-choice: Down and dirty*

1. **b)** Exchange; **2. b)** Digging down to two spade depths and adding organic

matter; **3. d)** Ericaceous; **4. c)** Acidic; **5. d)** 7.0; **6. a)** Nitrogen, phosphorus and potassium

Puzzle 19: *Plant parts*
1. Petal; **2.** Node; **3.** Axillary bud; **4.** Internode; **5.** Petiole; **6.** Root

Puzzle 20: *Multiple-choice: Biological brainteasers*
1. c) A growth hormone; **2. a)** Leaf fall; **3. b)** Lead bud over laterals; **4. b)** The movement of moisture from high concentration to low; **5. a)** Carrying water and minerals from the roots to the stems and leaves; **6. a)** The physical form and external structure of plants; **7. d)** Transpiration

Puzzle 21: *Mix and match: Taxing taxonomy*
1. D. Domain: Eukarya
2. H. Kingdom: Plantae
3. G. Division: Magnoliophyta
4. F. Class: Magnoliopsida
5. C. Order: *Rosales*
6. E. Family: *Rosaceae*
7. I. Genus: *Malus*
8. A. Species: *domestica*
9. B. Cultivar: 'Worcester Pearmain'

Puzzle 22: *Anatomy of a flower*
1. Petal; **2.** Stigma; **3.** Style; **4.** Sepal; **5.** Pedicel; **6.** Ovary; **7.** Filament; **8.** Anther

Puzzle 23: *Mix and match: Botanical breakthroughs*
1. D. Charles Darwin (British); **2. J.** Matthias Jakob Schleiden (German); **3. C.** Joseph Dalton Hooker (British); **4. F.** William Bartram (USA); **5. I.** Antoine Augustin Parmentier (French); **6. G.** Janaki Ammal (Indian); **7. B.** Carl Linnaeus (Swedish); **8. E.** Hugo von Mohl (German); **9. H.** Nikolai Vavilov (Russian); **10. A.** Jan Ingenhousz (Dutch)

Puzzle 24: *Anagrams: Scrambled science*
1. Dormancy; **2.** Cytokinins; **3.** Anthocyanins; **4.** Respiration; **5.** Germination; **6.** Gibberellins; **7.** Chlorophyll; **8.** Pollination; **9.** Pathogen; **10.** Vascular tissue

Answers
Chapter Three: Star Gardens

Puzzle 25: *Around the world in 10 gardens*
1. B. Jardim Botânico – Rio de Janeiro, Brazil (pale blue arrow); **2. F.** Shalimar Gardens – Lahore, Pakistan (dark blue arrow); **3. A.** Kirstenbosch National Botanic Garden – Cape Town, South Africa (pink arrow); **4. E.** Akatsuka Botanical Garden – Tokyo, Japan (brown arrow); **5. J.** Fairchild Tropical Botanic Garden – Miami, USA (red arrow); **6. H.** Jardin des Plantes – Paris, France (purple arrow); **7. D.** Nong Nooch Tropical Botanical Garden – Pattaya, Thailand (white arrow); **8. I.** Jardin d'Essais – Rabat, Morocco (green arrow); **9. G.** Patscherkofel Alpine Garden – Innsbruck, Austria (yellow arrow); **10. C.** Jardin de Cactus – Guatiza, Lanzarote, Canary Islands (orange arrow)

Puzzle 26: *Who am I?*
Vita Sackville-West

Puzzle 27: *Anagrams: Mixed-up gardens*
1. Royal Botanic Gardens, Kew;
2. Fallingwater; 3. Sítio Roberto Burle Marx; 4. Chateau de Villandry;
5. Le Jardin Majorelle; 6. Keukenhof Garden; 7. Munstead Wood;
8. The Summer Garden

Puzzle 28: *Multiple-choice: Gardens of the world*
1. b) Inverewe Garden; **2. a)** Piet Oudolf; **3. b)** Tatton Park;
4. d) Gravel, stones, moss;
5. a) The Butchart Gardens

Puzzle 29: *Identify the garden*
Monet's Garden, in Giverny, France

Puzzle 30: *Quick quiz: Know your gardens*
1. Canberra; 2. Sir Tim Smit;
3. William Shakespeare; 4. Dubai – the Dubai Miracle Garden; 5. South Africa; 6. They were all female;
7. *The Prisoner*; 8. Ornamental grasses

Puzzle 31: *What kind of garden am I?*

1. Westonbirt, England – arboretum;
2. Mount Vernon, USA – 18th-century landscape; **3.** Castle of Mey, Scotland – cottage garden; **4.** Bay Gardens, Grenada – tropical jungle;
5. Villa Medici, Italy – 15th-century Renaissance; **6.** Parc de Bagatelle, France – rose garden; **7.** Kenrokuen, Japan – stroll garden; **8.** Bagh-e Fin, Iran – Persian chahar bagh

Puzzle 32: *Which century?*

17th and 18th century
C. Felbrigg Hall, *Norfolk, England*
G. Oxford Botanic Garden, *Oxford, England*
H. Chateau de Fontainebleau, *Fontainebleau, France*
J. Levens Hall, *Cumbria, England*
N. Paleis Het Loo, *Amsterdam, Netherlands*
S. Stourhead, *Wiltshire, England*
T. Taj Mahal, *Agra, India*
19th century
B. Central Park, *New York, USA*
F. Rowallane Garden, *County Down, Ireland*
I. Biddulph Grange, *Stoke-on Trent, England*
K. The Lost Gardens of Heligan, *Cornwall, England*
M. Waddesdon Manor, *Buckinghamshire, England*

P. Gravetye Manor, *Sussex, England*
R. Tivoli, *Copenhagen, Denmark*
20th century
A. Mount Stewart, *County Down, Ireland*
D. Taliesin, *Wisconsin, USA*
E. The Garden of Cosmic Speculation, *Dumfries, Scotland*
L. Park Güell, *Barcelona, Spain*
O. La Pozas, *Xilitla, Mexico*
Q. Beth Chatto Gardens, *Essex, England*
U. Coleton Fishacre, *Devon, England*

Puzzle 33: *Mix and match:*
Famous for being famous
1. F. Prince Charles – Highgrove House; **2. C.** Anne Boleyn – Hever Castle; **3. A.** Beatrix Potter – Hill Top;
4. G. Thomas Jefferson – Monticello;
5. B. Frida Kahlo – Casa Azul;
6. H. Yves Saint Laurent – Jardin Majorelle; **7. E.** Empress Josephine – Chateau de Malmaison;
8. I. Winston Churchill – Chartwell;
9. D. Agatha Christie – Greenway

Puzzle 34: *Famous garden facts*
1. Ming; **2.** Cactus; **3.** Lambeth;
4. Harvard; **5.** Monsters

Puzzle 35: *What am I?*
Powerscourt Gardens, Enniskerry, County Wicklow, Ireland

Answers
Chapter Four: Around *the* World

Puzzle 36: *Mix and match: Global roots*

1. E. Petunia — South America;
2. H. Geranium — Southern Africa
and Australia; **3. F.** Garden sage —
Mediterranean; **4. B.** Zinnia —
The Americas, particularly Mexico;
5. G. Bougainvillea — Brazil/Argentina;
6. I. Phormium —New Zealand;
7. J. Rhubarb — China;
8. C. Apple — Central Asia;
9. D. Houseleek — Middle East;
10.A. Aspidistra — South East Asia

Puzzle 37: *Beyond borders*

1. Tundra
C. *Salix arctica*
K. *Silene acaulis*
Q. *Ledum groenlandium*
2. Taiga (also called boreal forest)
D. *Abies balsamea*
M. *Picea obovata*
V. *Larix sibirica*
3. Temperate deciduous forest
I. *Nothofagus dombeyi*
J. *Quercus robur*
U. *Acer pseudoplatanus*
**4. Scrubland (called chaparral
in California)**
L. *Eucalyptus gregsoniana*
W. *Myrtus communis*
X. *Artemisia abrotanum*

5. Grassland (savannah or prairie)
P. *Cynodon dactylon*
R. *Panicum virgatum*
O. *Pennisetum purpureum*
6. Desert
B. *Echinocactus grusonii*
H. *Beaucarnea recurvata*
A. *Agave americana*
7. Tropical rainforest
N. *Monstera deliciosa*
F. *Victoria amazonica*
G. *Rafflesia arnoldii*
8. Temperate rainforest
S. *Athyrium filix-femina*
T. *Polypodium glycyrrhiza*
E. *Pseudotsuga menziesii*

Puzzle 38: What am I?

1. *Dahlia*; **2.** *Diospyros kaki*;
3. *Dionaea muscipula* (Venus fly trap);
4. *Dieffenbachia* (dumb cane)

Puzzle 39: *National flowers*

1. Argentina; **2.** Switzerland;
3. Canada; **4.** India; **5.** Scotland;
6. Zimbabwe; **7.** Hong Kong;
8. Greece

**Puzzle 40: *Anagrams:
The mother of all gardens***

1. *Davidia involucrata* (handkerchief

tree); **2.** *Buddleja davidii* (butterfly bush); **3.** *Magnolia delavayi* (Delavay's magnolia); **4.** *Rosa chinensis* (China rose); **5.** *Anemone hupehensis* (Chinese anemone); **6.** *Rhododendron Fortunei*; **7.** *Phyllostachys edulis* (moso bamboo)

Puzzle 41: *What am I?*
Bamboo

Puzzle 42: *What am I?*
1. *Theobroma cacao* (cocoa); **2.** *Oryza sativa* (rice); **3.** *Actinidia deliciosa* (kiwifruit); **4.** *Hordeum vulgare* (barley)

Puzzle 43: *Which continent?*
1. America (*Carnegiea gigantea*);
2. Australia (*Acacia dealbata*);
3. Asia (*Hibiscus rosa-sinensis*);
4. Europe (*Hyacinthoides non-scripta*);
5. Africa (*Protea cynaroides*)

Puzzle 44: *Which country are we from?*
Mexico

Puzzle 45: *Multiple-choice: Wicked world*
1. b) *Strychnos nux-vomica*; **2. c)** *Conium maculatum*; **3. d)** *Nicotiana tabacum*; **4. b)** *Ricinus communis*

Puzzle 46: *Mediterranean marvels*
1. *Pistacia vera*; **2.** *Olea europaea*; **3.** *Laurus nobilis*; **4.** *Pinus pinea*; **5.** *Tulipa sylvestris*; **6.** *Rosmarinus officinalis*

Puzzle 47: *America versus Asia*
Americas
C. *Pseudotsuga menziesii*
E. *Helianthus annuus*
G. *Fuchsia magellanica*
J. *Victoria amazonica*
K. *Sequoiadendron giganteum*
M. *Passiflora caerulea*
N. *Amelanchier canadensis*
O. *Pinus radiata*
R. *Agave americana*
T. *Canna indica*
Asia
A. *Paeonia delavayi*
B. *Chaenomeles speciosa*
D. *Wisteria sinensis*
F. *Meconopsis betonicifolia*
H. *Viburnum farreri*
I. *Camellia saluenensis*
L. *Fatsia Japonica*
P. *Aucuba japonica*
Q. *Acer palmatum*
S. *Rhododendron sinogrande*

Puzzle 48: Island natives
1. F. *Catharanthus roseus* — Madagascar;
2. E. *Myosotidium hortensia* — Chatham Island; **3. D.** *Sorbus groenlandica* — Greenland; **4. G.** *Amorphophallus titanum* — Sumatra; **5. B.** *Gossypium darwinii* — Galapagos Islands; **6. I.** *Hedera azorica*- Azores; **7. A.** *Sasa nipponica* — Japan; **8. C.** *Acacia koa*- Hawaii; **9. J.** *Cerastium nigrescens*- Shetlands; **10. H.** *Richea pandanifolia* — Tasmania

Answers
Chapter Five: Through *the Ages*

Puzzle 49: *Mix and match:*
Whose garden?

1. G. Capability Brown – Stowe;
2. J. Sōami – Daisen-in Zen Garden;
3. C. André Le Nôtre – Versailles;
4. D. Lawrence Johnston – Hidcote
Manor; **5. H.** Muhammad ibn-Yusuf
ibn-Nash – Alhambra; **6. F.** Pietro
Bernini – Villa d'Este, Tivoli;
7. E. Shah Jahan – Shalimar;
8. B. Gertrude Jekyll – Munstead
Wood; **9. I.** Cyrus the Great –
Pasargadae Persian Gardens;
10. A. Claude Monet – Giverny

Puzzle 50: *Gardening titles*
1. E. Herbal; **2. D.** Flower;
3. G. Garden; **4. J.** Tempered;
5. C. Wild; **6. F.** Labyrinth;
7. H. Curious; **8. B.** Species;
9. I. Encyclopaedia; **10. A.** Forest

Puzzle 51: *Quick quiz: Garden pioneers*
1. St Fiacre; **2.** The infirmerer;
3. Charlemagne; **4.** Blue and gold;
5. The Domesday Book;
6. Gethsemane; **7.** Padua;
8. Francis Bacon; **9.** The Hanging
Gardens of Babylon; **10.** *Acanthus
spinosus*, or bear's breeches;
11. Xanadu; **12.** China

Puzzle 52: *Who am I?*
David Douglas

Puzzle 53: *Mix and match: Plant
hunters*
1. C. Joseph Dalton Hooker –
Antarctica, Himalayas, Middle
East, Western USA
2. A. Robert Brown – Australia
3. G. John Bartram – USA
4. E. Ynes Mexia – Mexico,
South America
5. D. Joseph Banks – Labrador,
Newfoundland, South Pacific
6. B. Francis Masson – Canaries,
Madeira, Azores, South Africa
7. F. Louis van Houtte – Brazil
8. I. Frank Kingdon-Ward –
China, Tibet
9. H. Joseph Martin – Mauritius,
Madagascar, Caribbean,
South Africa

Puzzle 54: *What am I?*
A lawnmower

Puzzle 55: *Anagrams:
Great garden designers*
1. Gilles Clément (France);
2. Pietro Porcinai (Italy); **3.** Joseph
Paxton (UK); **4.** Gustav Ammann

(Switzerland); **5.** Beatrix Cadwalader Farrand (USA); **6.** Ganna Walska (Poland); **7.** Friedrich Ludwig von Sckell (Germany); **8.** Peter Joseph Lenné (Prussia); **9.** Roberto Burle Marx (Brazil); **10.** Kate Middleton (UK)

Puzzle 56: *Multiple-choice: The golden age of the garden*
1. a) France; **2. c)** 64 – equivalent to the number of years of Queen Victoria's reign; **3. d)** 1861; **4. b)** Red; **5. c)** Wardian; **6. c)** Planting a grapevine at Hampton Court, which is now the largest in the world

Puzzle 57: *Anagrams: Garden styles*
1. Picturesque; **2.** Gardenesque; **3.** English landscape; **4.** Italian Renaissance; **5.** Arts and Crafts; **6.** Formal; **7.** English cottage garden; **8.** Naturalistic; **9.** French Baroque; **10.** Modernist

Puzzle 58: *Quick quiz: The time-travelling gardener*
1. *Fuchsia*; **2.** John Tradescant the Elder and Younger; **3.** Napoleon Bonaparte; **4.** The Linnaean Garden or Linnaeus' Garden; **5.** Red and white (Lancaster and York respectively); **6.** The Netherlands;

7. Chelsea Physic Garden; **8.** The RHS; **9.** Gnome; **10.** Suffragettes fighting for women's right to vote; **11.** Garden Organic; **12.** Carrot

Puzzle 59: *Multiple choice: Garden folly*
1. d) A covered walkway or porch; **2. a)** *Buxus sempervirens*, or box; **3. a)** Gargoyle (*gargouille* meaning throat); **4. c)** A shallow, narrow water feature; **5. d)** Gardenesque; **6. a)** A rock garden; **7. c)** Capability Brown; **8. c)** Ha-ha

Answers
Chapter Six: Greener Gardening

Puzzle 60: *Multiple-choice: Bird-brained*
1. a) Ornithology; **2. d)** Migrant;
3. d) Granivore; **4. c)** Oology;
5. b) Raptors; **6. d)** Flyway;
7. a) Pigeons and doves; **8. a)** Rachis;
9. c) Moulting; **10. c)** Finches;
11. d) Black oil seeds are more
nutritious; **12. b)** Clutch; **13. b)** Murder

Puzzle 61: *Quick quiz: Wildlife trivia*
1. Slug; **2.** Spiracles; **3.** Squirrel;
4. Six; **5.** Scales; **6.** Snake; **7.** Species;
8. Symbiosis

Puzzle 62: *Mix and match: We grow together*
1. E. Carrots – spring onions (the allium smell confuses flies that lay their eggs in this root crop);
2. G. Runner beans – sweet peas (attract more pollinating insects to improve setting of the pods);
3. B. Tomatoes – French marigolds (the strong smell deters whitefly, which can be a real problem with these fruits); **4. F.** Roses – garlic (helps to keep aphids away from these decorative shrubs and climbing beauties); **5. J.** Radish – mint (helps to deter flea beetles from attacking the leaves of this fast-growing, spicy root crop); **6. I.** Broad beans – summer savory (repels blackfly, a common pest of these legumes); **7. C.** Courgette – calendula (attracts pollinating insects to improve the yield of this summer vegetable); **8. H.** Sweetcorn – sunflowers (said to increase the yield and improve the sweetness of cobs, according to American growers);
9. A. Cabbage – chamomile (repels unwanted butterflies, preventing them from laying eggs on this leafy brassica); **10. D.** Strawberries – borage (deters pests, attracts beneficial

insects and saves time having two ingredients together when making a Pimm's cup)

Puzzle 63: *What am I?*
House sparrow

Puzzle 64: *The wildlife-friendly garden*
1. Wildlife pond; 2. Bird box; 3. Bug hotel; 4. Log pile; 5. Wildflower meadow; 6. Dead hedge; 7. Bee hive; 8. Native hedge; 9. Nettle patch; 10. Leaf pile

Puzzle 65: *Bug buddies*
1. Pollinators
C. Wasp (also a pest controller)
E. Solitary bee
G. Bumblebee
I. Butterfly
M. Honey bee
N. Hoverfly (also a pest controller)
2. Pest controllers
A. Green lacewing
D. Ladybird
J. Ground beetle
K. Parasitic wasp
P. Centipede
Enemies
B. Blackfly
F. Caterpillar
H. Scale
L. Slug
O. Thrip

Puzzle 66: *Planting for pollinators*
1. Clover (*Trifolium*); 2. Lime tree blossom (*Tilia*); 3. Buddleja; 4. Thyme (*Thymus*); 5. Ivy (*Hedera*); 6. Scabious (*Scabiosa*)

Puzzle 67: *Grow organic*
1. Soil; 2. Conditions; 3. Natural; 4. Environment; 5. Ecosystem; 6. Recycling; 7. Dig; 8. Fertilisers

Puzzle 68: *The good, the bad and the green*
1. Yellow trefoil (*Medicago lupulina*);
2. Buckwheat (*Fagopyrum esculentum*);
3. Field beans (*Vicia faba*);
4. Mustard (*Sinapis alba*);
5. Fenugreek (*Trigonella foenum-graecum*);
6. Alfalfa (*Medicago sativa*)

Puzzle 69: *Multiple-choice: How eco-savvy are you?*
1. **d)** Mulch; 2. **b)** It is semi-parasitic on grasses; 3. **d)** Bee 4. **b)** Peat; 5. **b)** Hedgehog; 6. **c)** Thinking about whole natural systems and sustainability; 7. **a)** Soft soap; 8. **d)** Seaweed

Puzzle 70: *What are we?*
Honey bees

Answers
Chapter Seven: The Fruit & Veg Patch

Puzzle 71: *Mix and match:*
Botanical beverages
1. C. Cognac – *Vitis vinifera* (grape vine);
2. D. Calvados – *Malus domestica* (apple);
3. A. Gin – *Juniperus communis* (juniper);
4. E. Tea – *Camellia sinensis* (tea plant);
5. J. Rum – *Saccharum officinarum* (sugar cane); **6. B.** Yerba maté – *Ilex paraguariensis* (Brazilian tea/maté);
7. I. Mudai – *Araucaria araucana* (monkey puzzle tree); **8. G.** Amarula – *Sclerocarya birrea* (marula); **9. H.** Rooibos – *Aspalathus linearis* (rooibos tea);
10. F. Crème de cassis – *Ribes nigrum* (blackcurrant)

Puzzle 72: What are we?
1. Shallot; **2.** Spinach; **3.** Starfruit;
4. Squash; **5.** Swede; **6.** Sweet potato;
7. Strawberry; **8.** Sage

Puzzle 73: Quick quiz: Herbal trivia
1. It has medicinal properties;
2. Parsley, sage, rosemary and thyme;
3. Stevia; **4.** Mint; **5.** Basil; **6.** Catnip;
7. It was thought dandelion could cause bed wetting; **8.** To make vegetable dyes; **9.** Elderflower and elderberry; **10.** Turmeric; **11.** Potato and tomato; **12.** Artichoke (globe and Jerusalem); **13.** Brussels sprout;

14. Kale (Jersey walking stick);
15. Corn, beans and squashes

Puzzle 74: Mix and match: Eat me
1. A. Potato – Tuber; **2. F.** Cinnamon – Bark; **3. J.** Tomato – Fruit;
4. E. Ginger – Rhizome; **5. G.** Broccoli – Florets; **6. B.** Cardamom – Seed pods; **7. I.** Fenugreek – Leaves;
8. H. Leeks – Stem; **9. C.** Saffron – Stigma; **10. D.** Poppy – Seed

Puzzle 75: Anagrams:
Higgledy-piggledy herbs
1. *Mentha arvensis* (wild mint); **2.** *Angelica archangelica* (angelica); **3.** *Laurus nobilis* (bay); **4.** *Rosmarinus officinalis* (rosemary);
5. *Petroselinum crispum* (parsley);
6. *Coriandrum sativum* (coriander);
7. *Thymus vulgaris* (thyme); **8.** *Ocimum basilicum* (basil)

Puzzle 76: Multiple-choice: Vegging out
1. d) Bean; **2. a)** Lacanophobia;
3. b) Chitting; **4. b)** Growing a different crop in a different vegetable bed each year; **5. c)** Asparagus;
6. d) Rhubarb; **7. a)** Scoville;
8. b) Tomato; **9. a)** Kernel;
10. d) Leaves and seeds; **11. b)** Citrus;
12. d) Runner

Puzzle 77: *Who's who in the veg garden?*

1. Legumes

B. Runner bean

O. Mange tout

H. Sugar snap

D. Borlotti

2. Brassicas

C. Cabbage

K. Brussel sprout

M. Kohlrabi

I. Turnip

3. Alliums

J. Elephant garlic

P. Onion

G. Shallot

A. Chives

4. Root crops

F. Carrot

L. Parsnip

E. Skirret

N. Salsify

Puzzle 78: *Multiple-choice: Fruity facts*

1. b) Cherry; **2. a)** Quince; **3. c)** M27;
4. c) Stool bush; **5. d)** A type of fig;
6. b) A dwarfing rootstock for
cherry trees

Puzzle 79: **What am I?**

Gooseberry (*Ribes uva-crispa*)

Puzzle 80: *Mix and match: Key ingredients*

1. K. French fries – Potato;

2. C. Sauerkraut – Cabbage;

3. F. Moussaka – Aubergine;

4. G. Houmous – Chickpea;

5. H. Tarte Normande – Apple;

6. I. Pesto – Basil;

7 .E. Guacamole – Avocado;

8. L. Marmalade – Seville orange;

9. B. Dhal – Lentil;

10. A. Clafoutis – Cherry;

11. J. Tzatziki – Cucumber;

12. D. Tabasco – Chilli

Puzzle 81: *Fruit IDs*

1. Date; **2.** Apricot; **3.** Mango;
4. Strawberry; **5.** Orange;
6. Nectarine; **Bonus fruit**: Damson

Puzzle 82: *Mix and match: Name that veg*

1. K. *Daucus – carota* (carrot);

2. E. *Cucumis – sativus* (cucumber);

3. F. *Cucurbita – pepo* (Courgette /
squash); **4. A.** *Beta – vulgaris* (beetroot);

5. C. *Apium – graveolens* (celery);

6. I. *Cichorium – intybus* (chicory);

7. J. *Zea – mays* (sweetcorn);

8. G. *Armoracia – rusticana* (horseradish);

9. D. *Pisum – sativum* (pea); **10. B.** *Solanum
– tuberosum* (potato); **11. L.** *Ipomoea –
batatas* (sweet potato); **12. H.** *Allium –
cepa* (onion)

Answers
Chapter Eight: Bugs & Beasties

Puzzle 83: *Quick quiz:*
Garden nightmares

1. Resistant; 2. Honeydew; 3. Chafer
grub; 4. Coral spot; 5. Reversion;
6. *Equisetum arvense*; 7. Chlorosis;
8. Slugs and snails; 9. Carrot fly;
10. Gall

Puzzle 84: *Mix and match: Diagnosis veg*

1. **G.** Blossom end rot – Tomatoes;
2. **D.** Clubroot – Cabbages;
3. **E.** Big bud mite – Blackcurrants;
4. **J.** Blackleg – Potatoes; 5. **F.** Green
top – Carrots; 6. **A.** Neck rot –
Onions; 7. **B.** Whiptail – Cauliflower;
8. **H.** Bitter pit – Apples;
9. **C.** American mildew –
Gooseberries; 10. **I.** Chocolate spot –
Broad beans

Puzzle 85: *What am I?*
Vine weevil (*Otiorhynchus sulcatus*)

Puzzle 86: *Fruit, flower, leaf, root*

1. Codling moth – fruit; 2. Eelworm –
root; 3. Verticillium wilt – leaf;
4. Pigeons – leaf; 5. Carrot fly – root;
6. Capsid bug – flower; 7. Slugworm –
leaf; 8. Petal blight – flower; 9. Brown
rot – fruit; 10. Tortrix moth – leaf

Puzzle 87: *Multiple-choice: Biosphere
blunders*

1. **c)** Australia; 2. **b)** *Phytophthora infestans*
(potato blight); 3. **d)** *Vitis vinifera*
(grapevine); 4. **c)** Carbon

Puzzle 88: *Most wanted line-up*
1. Spider mite; **2.** Aphid; **3.** Cutworm;
4. Earwig; **5.** Millipede; **6.** Wireworm;
7. Mealybug; **8.** Colorado beetle

Puzzle 89: *Six-letter nasties*
1. Mildew; **2.** Hopper; **3.** Beetle;
4. Canker; **5.** Blight; **6.** Thrips;
7. Silver

Puzzle 90: *Know your problem*
1. Pests
J. Whitefly
L. Mealybug
C. Scale
D. Larch adelgid
2. Diseases
K. Smut
E. Tulip fire
H. Shot hole
A. Potato spraing
3. Disorders
B. Waterlogging
F. Oedema
G. Corky scab
I. Fasciation

Puzzle 91: *Multiple-choice: Plant plight*
1. d) Rhizome rot; **2. d)** Slime flux;
3. d) Agapanthus gall midge;
4. b) Fireblight; **5. c)** Clubroot

Puzzle 92: *Fill the blanks: Winning the battle*
1. Pheromone; **2.** Systemic; **3.** Prevention;
4. Certified; **5.** Copper; **6.** Besom;
7. Hygiene; **8.** Collars; **9.** Splitting;
10. Flowerpots

Puzzle 93: *Anagrams: Chemical-free critter control*
1. Caterpillar; **2.** Vine weevil; **3.** Spider mite; **4.** Whitefly; **5.** Slug; **6.** Aphids;
7. Mealybug; **8.** Fungus gnat

Puzzle 94: *Lawn troubles*
1. Leatherjacket; **2.** Fairy ring;
3. Worms; **4.** Fusarium; **5.** Red thread;
6. Fertiliser scorch

Puzzle 95: *What am I?*
Phytophthora ramorum — the cause of sudden oak death

Answers
Chapter Nine: Branching Out

Puzzle 96: *To climb or not to climb*

Choisya ternata, *Cotinus coggygria* and *Fatsia japonica*

Puzzle 97: *Colour comrades*

1. White

D. *Magnolia grandiflora*

J. *Viburnum opulus*

K. *Yucca gloriosa*

2. Yellow

F. *Cornus mas*

G. *Hypericum perforatum*

I. *Forsythia intermedia*

3. Blue

H. *Ceanothus impressus*

L. *Ceratostigma willmottianum*

E. *Perovskia atriplicifolia*

4. Red

B. *Crinodendron hookerianum*

C. *Embothrium coccineum*

A. *Paeonia delavayi*

Puzzle 98: *Quick quiz: Wooded wonders*

1. Lewis Carroll; **2.** Japanese Maple; **3.** William Lobb; **4.** *Prunus serrula*; **5.** Apical dominance; **6.** Goat willow; **7.** *Trachycarpus fortunei*; **8.** Bare root; **9.** Christmas tree; **10.** Wollemi pine

Puzzle 99: *Mix and match: Small but stunning*

1. D. *Cornus — mas* (cornelian); **2. F.** *Magnolia — soulangeana* (saucer); **3. G.** *Pyrus — salicifolia* 'Pendula' (weeping pear); **4. A.** *Parrotia — persica* (Persian ironwood); **5. B.** *Robinia — pseudoacacia* (false acacia); **6. H.** *Rhus — typhina* (staghorn sumac); **7. I.** *Ligustrum — lucidum* (privet); **8. E.** *Koelreuteria — paniculata* (golden rain tree); **9. J.** *Crataegus — laevigata* (English hawthorn); **10. C.** *Cotinus — coggygria* (smoke bush)

Puzzle 100: *Bushy botanical names*

1. *Hippophae rhamnoides*; **2.** *Osmanthus burkwoodii*; **3.** *Rhododendron ponticum*; **4.** *Nothofagus*; **5.** *Betula utilis* var. *jacquemontii*; **6.** *Eriobotrya japonica*; **7.** *Acacia dealbata*; **8.** *Mahonia japonica*

Bonus answer: Hornbeam

Puzzle 101: *Mix and match: Animal attraction*

1. C. Monkey — puzzle (*Araucaria araucana*); **2. H.** Dog — wood (*Cornus*); **3. G.** Horse — chestnut (*Aesculus hippocastanum*); **4. A.** Snake — bark (*Acer davidii*); **5. I.** Butterfly — bush (*Buddleja davidii*); **6. E.** Goose — berry (*Ribes*); **7. J.** Mule — fat (*Baccharis salicifolia*);

8. F. Lion's – tail *(Leonotis leonurus)*;
9. B. Elephant – ear *(Acacia dunnii)*;
10. D. Bat face – flower *(Cuphea llavea)*

Puzzle 102: *Functional flora*
1. Late spring- and summer-flowering shrubs
C. *Philadelphus coronarius*
G. *Weigela florida*
B. *Deutzia × rosea*
2. Colourful autumn foliage
H. *Acer palmatum*
K. *Liquidambar styraciflua*
L. *Nyssa sinensis*
3. Winter-flowering shrubs
A. *Chimonanthus praecox*
N. *Lonicera fragrantissima*
M. *Sarcococca humilis*
4. Winter stems
D. *Cornus sanguinea* 'Midwinter Fire'
F. *Salix alba* subsp. *vitellina* 'Britzensis'
I. *Rubus cockburnianus*
5. Edible fruit
E. *Malus domestica*
J. *Pyrus communis*
O. *Prunus armeniaca*

Puzzle 103: *Multiple-choice: Tree trivia*
1. a) *Camellia sasanqua*; **2. d)** Blue;
3. b) Having the most painful sting in the world; **4. a)** *Acer*; **5. b)** *Sequoia sempervirens*; **6. b)** Cherry tree blossom;
7. b) The flower bracts look like handkerchiefs; **8. a)** Ornamental, coppery-coloured, peeling bark;

9. d) European ash;
10. c) Aromatic leaves; **11. a)** *Magnolia grandiflora*; **12. c)** Tree fern

Puzzle 104: *Anagrams: Confused conifers*
1. *Abies grandis*; **2.** *Metasequoia glyptostroboides*; **3.** *Microbiota decussata*;
4. *Thuja plicata*; **5.** *Taxodium distichum*;
6. *Juniperus communis*; **7.** *Chamaecyparis lawsoniana*; **8.** *Taxus baccata*

Puzzle 105: *What am I?*
Morus nigra (black mulberry)

Puzzle 106: *What type?*
1. Climbers
A. *Aristolochia elegans*; **D.** *Passiflora edulis*
G. *Hedera helix*; **I.** *Rosa* 'Zéphirine Drouhin'
2. Large trees
C. *Fagus sylvatica*; **E.** *Larix occidentalis*;
H. *Quercus robur*; **L.** *Acer saccharinum*
3. Shrubs
B. *Lavandula angustifolia*; **F.** *Daphne bholua*;
J. *Desfontainia spinosa*; **K.** *Calluna vulgaris*

Puzzle 107: Literary trees
1. *The Wind in the Willows*; **2.** *The Children of Cherry Tree Farm*; **3.** *Chestnut Street*;
4. *Children of the Jacaranda Tree*; **5.** *Under the Greenwood Tree*; **6.** *Sad Cypress*; **7.** *Cedar Valley*; **8.** *The Ivy Tree*; **9.** *And to Think That I Saw It on Mulberry Street*; **10.** *Under the Baobab Tree*

Answers
Chapter Ten: The Flowerbed

Puzzle 108: *Mix and match:*
Flora and fauna
1. E. Foxtail – lily; **2. B.** Wolf's – bane;
3. J. Buffalo – grass; **4. C.** Cat – mint;
5. D. Bee – orchid; **6. H.** Kangaroo
– paw; **7. F.** Toad – flax; **8. A.** Bear's
– breeches; **9. G.** Cow – slip; **10. I.**
Worm – wood

Puzzle 109: *Know your leaves*
1. E. Heuchera; **2. F.** Delphinium;
3. A. Lupin; **4. H.** Gunnera;
5. D. Sage; **6. B.** Hosta;
7. G. Peony; **8. C.** Acanthus

Puzzle 110: *Quick quiz: Bedding beauties*
1. Allium; **2.** They are both called
marigolds; **3.** William Wordsworth;
4. Lily; **5.** Snowdrops; **6.** Field poppy;
7. Strawberry; **8.** Daffodil (*Narcissus*);
9. Honesty (*Lunaria annua*);
10. Colchicum; **11.** They grow over
two years; **12.** Carnation (*Dianthus*);
13. Spanish moss (*Tillandsia usneoides*);
14. Sweet pea (*Lathyrus odorata*);
15. Dyer's woad (*Isatis tinctorium*);
16. Damp shade

Puzzle 111: *What type of plant?*
1. Bulbs
B. *Galanthus nivalis*
E. *Tulipa* spp.
K. *Hyacinthus orientalis*
N. *Narcissus pseudonarcissus*
Ornamental grasses
A. *Festuca glauca*
D. *Cortaderia selloana*
G. *Pennisetum villosum*
M. *Stipa tenuissima*
Herbaceous perennial border
H. *Anemone hybrida*
I. *Echinacea purpurea*
L. *Delphinium elatum*
O. *Hosta sieboldii*
Annuals or tender perennials
C. *Cosmos bipinnatus*
F. *Tropaeolum majus*
J. *Clarkia amoena*
P. *Lathyrus odoratus*

Puzzle 112: *Novel plants*
1. *The Catcher in the Rye*, **2.** *The Black Tulip*;
3. *The Name of the Rose*; **4.** *Driving Miss
Daisy*; **5.** *Rosemary's Baby*; **6.** *The Scarlet
Pimpernel*; **7.** *Daisy-Head Mayzie*; **8.** *The Lady
of the Camellias*; **9.** *Dandelion Wine*;
10. *The Lily of the Valley*

Puzzle 113: *Multiple-choice:*
Plant peculiarities
1. b) Poached egg plant; **2. c)** *Begonia semperflorens* (wax begonia);
3. a) Ultraviolet; **4. b)** *Betula utilis*;
5. d) *Narcissus pseudonarcissus*;
6. d) *Euphorbia epithymoides*; **7. b)** 17;
8. d) Cherry pie; **9. d)** *Pelargonium grandiflorum*; **10. a)** Impatiens downy mildew; **11. c)** Its leaves fold and droop when touched

Puzzle 114: *Guess the plant*
1. Aster; **2.** Chrysanthemum;
3. Hosta; **4.** Iris; **5.** Lathyrus;
6. Leucojum; **7.** Echinacea;
8. Amaryllis
Bonus answer: Achillea

Puzzle 115: *What am I?*
Sunflower

Puzzle 116: *Colour categories*
1. Yellow
D. *Primula vulgaris*
E. *Digitalis lutea*
L. *Narcissus* 'Tête-à-tête'
2. Black
G. *Tulipa* 'Queen of Night'
H. *Viola* 'Molly Sanderson'
I. *Iris* 'Before the Storm'

3. Red
A. *Dahlia* 'Bishop of Llandaff'
C. *Crocosmia* 'Lucifer'
J. *Papaver rhoeas*
4. Blue
B. *Centaurea montana*
F. *Perovskia atriplicifolia*
K. *Hyacinthoides non-scripta*

Puzzle 117: *Anagrams: Flowerbed favourites*
1. Penstemon; **2.** Aster; **3.** Daisy;
4. Tulip; **5.** Violet; **6.** Agapanthus;
7. Zinnia; **8.** Dahlia

Puzzle 118: *Mix and match:*
Garden heroes
1. J. *Eschscholzia — californica* (California poppy); **2. E.** *Campanula — latifolia* (giant bellflower); **3. L.** *Achillea — millefolium* (yarrow); **4. F.** *Digitalis — purpurea* (foxglove); **5. G.** *Foeniculum — vulgare* (fennel); **6. B.** *Fritillaria — imperialis* (crown imperial); **7. H.** *Lilium — tigrinum* (tiger lily); **8. I.** *Melianthus — major* (honey bush); **9. D.** *Phormium — tenax* (New Zealand flax);
10. A. *Salvia — elegans* (pineapple sage);
11. C. *Stachys — byzantina* (lamb's ears);
12. K. *Strelitzia — reginae* (bird of paradise)

Puzzle 119: *Picture perfect*
1. *Salvia*; **2.** *Stipa*; **3.** *Sempervivum*;
4. *Saxifraga*; **5.** *Sedum*; **6.** *Senecio*

Answers
Chapter Eleven: Back *to* Basics

Puzzle 120: *Where in the garden?*
1. **H.** Mixed border; **2. G.** Kitchen garden; **3. D.** Potting shed; **4. C.** Greenhouse; **5. K.** Green roof; **6. F.** Woodland garden; **7. L.** Herbaceous border; **8. B.** Raised bed; **9. J.** Hanging basket; **10. E.** Knot garden; **11. I.** Water feature; **12. A.** Compost heap

Puzzle 121: *Weeding worries*
1. Perennial
B. Bramble (*Rubus fruticosus*)
F. Bindweed (*Convolvulus arvensis*)
G. Stinging nettle (*Urtica dioica*)
H. Dandelion (*Taraxacum officinale*)
J. Ground elder (*Aegopodium podagraria*)
2. Annual
A. Groundsel (*Senecio vulgaris*)
C. Annual meadow grass (*Poa annua*)
D. Hairy bittercress (*Cardamine hirsuta*)
E. Chickweed (*Stellaria media*)
I. Fat hen (*Chenopodium album*)

Puzzle 122: *Multiple-choice: Green, green grass*
1. b) Yucca; **2. a)** Aeration; **3. c)** Switch; **4. d)** Scarification; **5. a)** Besom; **6. b)** Dead and decaying grass and other organic matter at the base of grass plants

Puzzle 123: *From the tool shed*
1. Half moon; **2.** Edging shears; **3.** Lawn lute; **4.** Wheelbarrow; **5.** Brushcutter; **6.** Leaf blower; **7.** Garden fork; **8.** Drop spreader

Puzzle 124: *Put your finger on it*
1. Deadheading; **2.** Pinching out; **3.** Chip budding; **4.** Double digging; **5.** Potting on; **6.** Heeling in; **7.** Thinning out; **8.** Formative pruning

Puzzle 125: *Fill the blanks: New life*
1. Division; **2.** Hardwood cutting; **3.** Heel cutting; **4.** Micro propagation; **5.** Sowing; **6.** Whip and tongue; **7.** Softwood cutting; **8.** Semi-ripe cutting; **9.** Layering; **10.** Twin scaling

Puzzle 126: *Shapely shrubs and trees*
1. E. Cordon; **2. D.** Espalier; **3. A.** Pollard; **4. F.** Coppice; **5. B.** Fan; **6. C.** Pleached

Puzzle 127: *Multiple-choice:*
Terminology test
1. a) Bypass and anvil; **2. b)** Restorative
pruning; **3. d)** Nicking and notching;
4. c) A method for late-summer
pruning of fruit trees; **5. c)** A shoot
for grafting onto a rootstock;
6. b) Forcing;

7. d) A bell-shaped cover placed over
plants for protection; **8. a)** Shaping
bushes into cloud shapes;
9. c) Building up layers of different
compost materials in a bed;
10. c) A keyhole-shaped raised bed
with a compost heap in the middle;
11. b) Soil; **12. b)** A type of no-dig
raised bed

**Puzzle 128: Complete your own
A to Z glossary**
Axil; Blanching; Clamp; Damping
down; Etiolation; Friable; Grafting;
Hardening off; Irrigation; John
Innes; Knot garden; Leaf mould;
Mycorrhizae; Nectar;
Oxygenator; Pricking out;
Quartered rosette; Rain
shadow; Sucker; Topiary;
Underplanting;
Vermiculite; Water butt;
Xerophyte; Year; Zoonose

Picture Credits

B = bottom, C = center, L = left, R = right, T =top

Cover and pages 9–10, 24–25, 40–41, 56–57, 72–73, 88–99, 102–103, 118–119, 134–135, 150–151, 166–167 all © Leila Divine | Shutterstock

Pages 1 Doremi; 10 Krumao; 19 KEEP GOING; 22 spline_x; 24 (TL) Marc Roura; 27 (TC) Skyprayer2005; 27 (TR) mizy; 27 (CL) Erik Agar; 27 (C) pangcom; 27 (CR) Daniel Poloha; 27 (BL) Zulashai; 27 (BR) simona pavan; 32, 82, 124–125, 125 (TR), 177 Morphart Creation; 42–43 Tanarch; 47 (TL) FreeProd33; 47 (TR) Oleg Bakhirev; 47 (BL) andre quinou; 47 (BR) Julneighbour; 63 AVA Bitter; 69 Lyubov Tolstova; 114 RAndrei; 126 (TL) Catherine Eckert; 126 (TC) schankz; 126 (TR) kale kkm; 126 (CL) Frauenversand Cleopatra; 126 (C) SUPAPORNKH; 126 (CR) Meg Sopki; 126 (BL) FCerez; 126 (BR) Oleksandrum/Shutterstock; 132 (TC) JohnatAPW; 132 (TR) Thanthip Homs; 132 (BL) Tunatura; 132 (BR) photowind; 153 (T: L–R) gianpihada, SeDmi, Rob Stark, Richard Griffin; 153 (B: L–R) spline_x, ArtCookStudio, Lepas, flaviano fabrizi; 161 Invisible Studio; 165 (TC) Africa Studio; 165 (TR) pjhpix; 165 (BL) Matthewshutter; 165 (BC) picturepartners; 165 (BR) Richard Griffin; 168 (TL) Sally Wallis; 168 (TC) Irina Fischer; 168 (TR) Del Boy; 168 (BL) a40757; 168 (BC) josefkubes; 168 (BR) Jon Bilous; 169 (TL) Adam Fraise; 169 (TC) Del Boy; 169 (TR) Arina P Habich; 169 (BL) David Hughes; 169 (BC) Anita Warren-Hampson; 169 (BR) LianeM; 172 (TL) Stacey Newman; 172 (TC) JaneHYork; 172 (CL) Artorn Thongtuki; 172 (C) Lubos K; 172 (CR) Saklakova; 172 (BL) Miriam Doerr Martin Frommherz; 172 (BR) photowind; 173 (TL) Jason Kolenda; 173 (TC) Floki; 173 (TR) suthin supanbud; 173 (C) IgorAleks; 173 (BL) Denis Pogostin; 175 (TL) Andrew Fletcher; 175 (TC) Andrew Fletcher; 175 (TR) Ruud Morijn Photographer; 175 (BL) AngieC333; 175 (BC) Deatonphotos all © Shutterstock

Pages 2, 11 (TL, TC, BL, BC), 13 (TL, BL, BR), 15 (TL, BR), 16, 17 (L, R), 20 (TL, TC, BL, BC), 23 (TC, TR, BC, BR), 26, 28, 29, 30, 33, 36, 37, 45, 61, 65 (TR), 68 (TC, BR), 77, 83, 93, 97 (TC, TR), 105 (TR, BL), 108, 113, 115, 116 (TC, BC), 117 (R), 129, 136 (L, R), 137, 138, 139 (L), 142, 145, 146, 155, 156, 157 (L), 160, 163, 165 (TL, BL, BC, BR), 170, 171, 186 all © plantillustrations.org

Pages 4, 21, 75, 116, 148, 157 (R), 159 all © RHS Images

Pages 31 Biodiversity Heritage Library; 52 (TL) Dan Marsh; 78, 131 Biodiversity Heritage Library; 86, 107, 111, 147 Wellcome Images; 132 (BC) Kris Lord all Creative Commons

Page 52 (TR) © Express Newspapers/Getty Images

Pages 52 (CR) Trinity Mirror/Mirror Pix; 55 Art Collection 3; 74 Archivist; 87 Colin Waters; 110 Quagga Media; 116 (TL) Florilegius; 132 (TL) Nigel Cattlin; 139 (R) Historical image collection by Bildagentur-online; 141, 205 Botanical art/ Bildagentur-online; 152 Florilegius; 165 (TL) Sergii Koval; 172 (TR) Dorling Kindersley Ltd; 173 (CL) Dorling Kindersley ltd; 173 (CR) Gary K Smith; 173 (BR) Deborah Vernon; 175 (BR) RM Floral; 180 Walker Art Library; 205 Historic Collection all © Alamy Stock Photo

Page 67 © BioLib

All other images in this book are in the public domain.

Every effort has been made to credit the copyright holders of the images used in this book. The publisher apologises for any unintentional omissions or errors and will insert the appropriate acknowledgement to any companies or individuals in subsequent editions of the work.

Further Reading

BOOKS

RHS Botany for Gardeners: The Art and Science of Gardening Explained and Explored. London: Mitchell Beazley, 2013

Akeroyd, Simon, and Dr Ross Bayton. *RHS Gardening School.* London: Mitchell Beazley, 2018

Biggs, Matthew. *RHS The Secrets of Great Botanists.* London: Mitchell Beazley, 2018

James, Matt. *RHS How to Plant a Garden.* London: Mitchell Beazley, 2016

Baker, Harry. *Fruit Garden Displayed* (9th edn). Boston, MA: Cengage Learning, 1980

Klein, Carol. *Grow Your Own Vegetables.* London: Mitchell Beazley, 2008

McVicar, Jekka. *Jekka's Complete Herb Book.* London: Kyle Books, 2009

Robinson, William. *The Wild Garden.* Portland, OR: Timber Press, 2010

Kingsbury, Noel, and Piet Oudolf. *Planting: A new perspective.* Portland, OR: Timber Press, 2013

Gardiner, Jim. *Encyclopaedia of Flowering Shrubs.* Portland, OR: Timber Press, 2012

Akeroyd, Simon. *The Good Gardener.* London: Pavilion Books/National Trust, 2015

RHS. Allotment Handbook and Planner. London: Mitchell Beazley, 2015

Brickell, Chris, and David Joyce. *RHS Pruning and Training.* London: DK, 2017

Brickell, Chris (ed). *RHS Encyclopaedia of Gardening* (3rd edn). London: DK, 2007

Greenwood, Pippa, and Andrew Halstead. *RHS Pests and Diseases.* London: DK, 2018

Maughan, Simon. *RHS Genealogy for Gardeners.* London: Mitchell Beazley, 2017

Toogood, Alan. *RHS Propagating plants.* London: DK, 2019

Young, Chris. *RHS Encyclopaedia of Garden Design.* London: DK, 2017

Harrison, Lorraine. *RHS Latin for Gardeners.* London: Mitchell Beazley, 2012

Bradbury, Kate. *Wildlife Gardening.* London: Bloomsbury/Wildlife Trusts, 2019

Johnson, Hugh. *The Hugh Johnson International Book of Trees.* London: Mitchell Beazley, 1999

ONLINE RESOURCES

Garden Organic: www.gardenorganic.org.uk

The Gardens Trust: www.thegardenstrust.org/about-us

National Plant Collections: www.nccpg.com

National Trust: www.nationaltrust.org.uk

RHS gardening advice: www.rhs.org.uk

Society of Garden Designers: www.sgd.org.uk

About the Authors

Simon Akeroyd is the author of *RHS Gardening School* and the *RHS Allotment Handbook and Planner* (both Mitchell Beazley). He was previously a Garden Manager for the Royal Horticultural Society, and worked at both RHS Wisley and Harlow Carr.

Dr Gareth Moore is a puzzle expert who has authored numerous bestselling books, including the enduringly popular *Ordnance Survey Puzzle Book* and *The Penguin Book of Puzzles*.